Cloudburst

A Handbook of
Rural Skills &
Technology

Cloudburst

A Handbook of
Rural Skills & Technology

Revised Edition

Edited by Vic Marks

Illustrated by Ted Turner

Cloudburst Press
Mayne Island & Seattle
1977

Published
In Canada by:
Cloudburst Press Ltd.
Mayne Island, B.C. V0N 2J0
Published in the United States of America by:
Cloudburst Press of America, Inc:
85 South Washington Street
Seattle, Washington
98104

ISBN 0-88930-016-X (softcover)
ISBN 0-88930-038-0 (hardcover)
©1973,1977 by Cloudburst Press Ltd.

All Rights Reserved
Printed in the U.S.A.
1st Printing, April 1973
6th Printing, October 1976
Revised Edition—1st Printing, September 1977
This book may be ordered from the
publisher by sending the cover
price plus twenty-five cents
for shipping to either of
the addresses above.

Distributed to the
trade in the U.S.A. by:
The Stephen Greene Press
Brattleboro, Vermont 05301
Distributed to the trade in Canada by:
J.J. Douglas Ltd., Publishers,
1875 Welch Street
North Vancouver, B.C.
V7P 1B7

CAMROSE LUTHERAN COLLEGE
Library

TH
148
C
628
/25,023

Credits

Thanks are extended to the following authors and publishers as sources of the articles listed below.

Harnessing the Small Stream reprinted courtesy of Popular Science Monthly, 355 Lexington Avenue, New York, N.Y. ©1947 by Popular Science Publishing Co. Inc.

The Michell Turbine reprinted from Low-Cost Development of Small Waterpower Sites, VITA, College Campus, Schenectady, N.Y.

Frost Damage Prevention reprinted from Five Acres and Independence by M.G. Kains, Greenburg, N.Y.

A Treadle Driven Wood Turning Lathe reprinted from 40 Power Tools You can Make, Popular Mechanics Press, Chicago, Illinois.

How to Build an Indian Berry Picker reprinted from the Northwest Passage, P.O. Box 105, S. Bellingham Station, Bellingham, Washington

A Solar Dryer adapted from How to Make a Solar Cabinet Dryer from Agricultural Produce by T.A. Laward. Available from: Brace Research Institute, Faculty of Engineering, McGill University, Montreal 2, P.Q., Canada.

Table of Drying Times and Methods in *A Solar Dryer* article reprinted from Mother Earth News, No. 10, Box 90, Henderson, North Carolina.

How to Build a Juice Press reprinted from Farmer's Bulletin, No. 114, Canada Department of Agriculture, Ottawa, Canada.

The Smoke Curing and Salting of Fish reprinted from Smokehouses and the Smoke Curing of Fish by Iola I. Burg, Washington Department

of Fisheries, Olympia, Washington.

How to Salt Fish reprinted from Village Technology Handbook, VITA, College Campus, Schenectady, N.Y.

Cheesemaking by Monica Rice, Elsie Evelsizer and Helen Valentine, reprinted from the Northwest Passage, P.O. Box 105, S. Bellingham Station, Bellingham, Washington, and The Green Revolution, Heathcote Road, Freeland, Maryland.

Rural Water Works reprinted from Farmer's Bulletin No. 927, U.S. Department of Agriculture, Washington, D.C.

A Hand Operated Washing Machine reprinted from Village Technology Handbook, VITA, College Campus, Schenectady, N.Y.

Contents

About this series...

Cloudburst, a handbook of rural skills and technology, is a book born of people's experiences; people who are finding ways of living harmoniously with nature rather than exploiting it; people who are seeking to think small in a world overrun by big thinking; people who are forming lifestyles based on the economics of semi-sufficiency. Cloudburst is an introduction to the arts/skills/technologies of living and working on the land. It attempts to cover with depth some of the basic problems facing the growing movement of people seeking to decentralize society and re-populate the countryside. As such, it gets a lot of its impetus from days gone by; from the crafts/skills/technologies of the last 100 years which have been glossed over in our pursuit of "high" technology. The regaining of forgotten knowledge shall be the foundation on which we build a harmonious societal structure, based on the use of low impact or intermediate technology and skills. The intention of Cloudburst is to be a vehicle for the sharing of past and present skills, and rain for the garden of knowledge which must grow if we are to survive the drought of twentieth-century thinking.

Cloudburst 2 (available from Cloudburst Press or any bookstore) contains designs for a solar roof water heater, a honey extractor, a chicken guillotine, a leaf and hay baler, a table loom, spinning wheels, a wool carder, a wood fired kiln, an outdoor rock stove, a foot powered scroll saw, a hydraulic ram, a sunpit greenhouse, an indoor waterless toilet, a one pony sled, and an eco-cabin. Also included are techniques for falling timber, building sod, hay, and post and beam outbuildings and of course, much more.

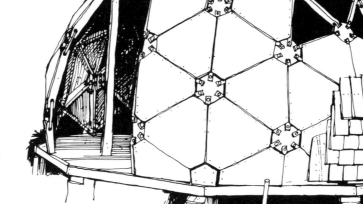

by Jim Bohlen
& Russ Chernoff

The 16ft. Personal Dome

The Personal Dome was designed to offer privacy and flexibility for internal arrangements of space. Its structure allows for interconnection with other domes (fig. 1).

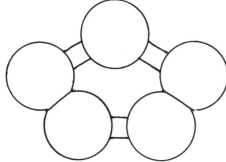

FIGURE 1

The Personal Dome geometry was derived from the dodecahedron, which consists of 12 pentagons (fig. 2a). This polygon was chosen as it yields strut locations which allow access to the interior with minimum disturbance of the structural elements. The Personal Dome is 6/10 of a spherical dodecahedron or a "6/10 sphere" (fig 2b), which is a "natural" division and requires dealing with only one odd-length strut. A rather large number of sub-divisions of the triangles was selected, as it facilitates in-stallation of such things as doors, windows, sheathing, insulation, and affords geometric similarity. The side struts rising from the foundation are essentially vertical, and provide generous standup room along the dome per-imeter on the inside. The geometric similarity permits five evenly-spaced access portals, which are important to

have when considering the community assembly of domes. Individuality of design will result from solutions to localized environmental problems. For instance, con-sider a community of personal domes, joined with pas-sageways: the form and shape of the passages will be determined by the terrain and the unique social aspects of each community.

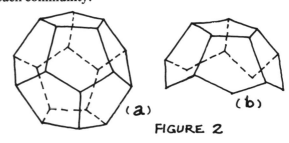

FIGURE 2

The Dodecahedron

Before proceeding farther, we should define the ele-mental geodesic terms. *Frequency* denotes how each pentagon is broken down. The Personal Dome is a two frequency dome.

FIGURE 3

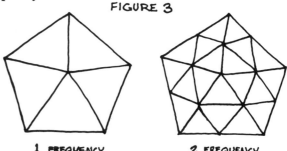

1 FREQUENCY   2 FREQUENCY

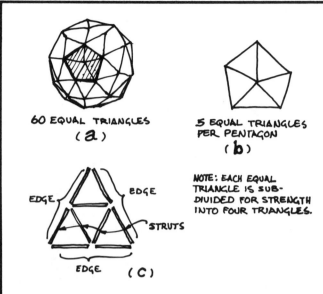

60 EQUAL TRIANGLES
(a)

5 EQUAL TRIANGLES
PER PENTAGON
(b)

NOTE: EACH EQUAL
TRIANGLE IS SUB-
DIVIDED FOR STRENGTH
INTO FOUR TRIANGLES.

EDGE   EDGE
EDGE
STRUTS
EDGE   (c)

FIGURE 4

A spherical one frequency dodecahedron consists of 12 pentagons or 60 equal triangles—each pentagon containing 5 of the 60 triangles (figs. 4a and 4b). In a two frequency dodecahedron, each of these triangles breaks down into 4 smaller triangles, making 240 triangles total. To visualize this, start with one of the 60 triangles in the one frequency dodecahedron. It has three edges (fig. 4c) and it is subdivided into four smaller triangles by dividing each edge in two (this is done in such a way that the edges will begin to curve outward—fig. 5.). Dividing each edge in two gives you more strength. As you increase the frequency, you get closer to a sphere (and increase the stand-up floor area as well).

1 FREQUENCY   2 FREQUENCY   3 FREQUENCY

FIGURE 5

The *struts* are the pieces of material out of which the geometric framework is constructed; in figure 4c for example, each line is a strut and there are nine struts altogether.

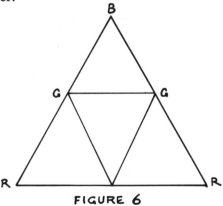

FIGURE 6

The *strut length* is determined by deducting a uniform dimension from each hub-to-hub distance. This dimension is determined from the specific hub design (figs. 8, 9, and 10).

For the two frequency dodecahedron there are 4 strut lengths (fig. 6 and table 1). Multiply the chord factor (column 3, table 1) by the radius in inches; then deduct 6-1/4-in. from that number. This will be the strut length for the hub design which is included. In this same manner, any size dome may be calculated.

The struts are connected to each other by *hubs*. These connecting hubs are made of 3/4-in. exterior-grade plywood (e.g., used concrete forms). The connectors are made of hardwood dowels which are shaped into 3/4-in. diameter pegs. The hubs are inserted into the sawn slots at the ends of the struts, and the pegs are pushed into place (fig. 7). The holes are all pre-drilled to give the necessary precision and therefore to assure ease of assembly and structural integrity.

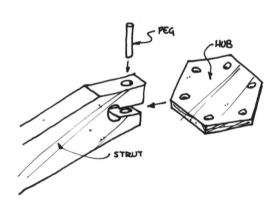

PEG
HUB
STRUT

FIGURE 7

Strut Construction

The struts are made from 2 x 4's cut to the exact strut length (table 1). Code the ends B, G, or R, as the case may be. Try to cut the material so that knots in the wood are avoided at the ends where the slots, the slot holes, and the peg holes will be cut (fig. 7). After making a few of the complete struts, place them on the plan (fig.-12) to conform with the outline of the strut end as shown to check your workmanship. Inaccuracies in the beginning will be paid for later when assembling the dome frame in the field.

If dowels cannot be purchased, they can be made by driving a stick of hardwood through a block of steel which has the proper size holes drilled in it. Another feature of the hub design is that poles may be substituted for dimension lumber. This alternative can be important in the bush.

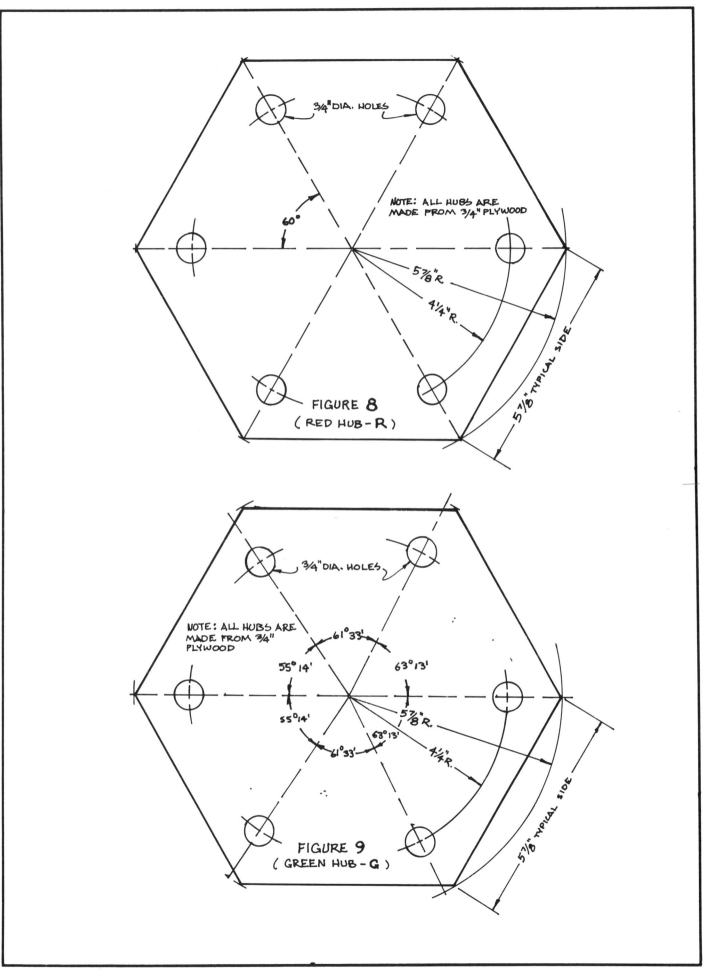

FIGURE 8
(RED HUB - R)

NOTE: ALL HUBS ARE MADE FROM 3/4" PLYWOOD

3/4" DIA. HOLES

60°

5 7/8" R.

4 1/4" R.

5 7/8 TYPICAL SIDE

FIGURE 9
(GREEN HUB - G)

NOTE: ALL HUBS ARE MADE FROM 3/4" PLYWOOD

3/4" DIA. HOLES

61° 33'

55° 14'

63° 13'

55° 14'

63° 13'

61° 33'

5 7/8" R.

4 1/4" R.

5 7/8 TYPICAL SIDE

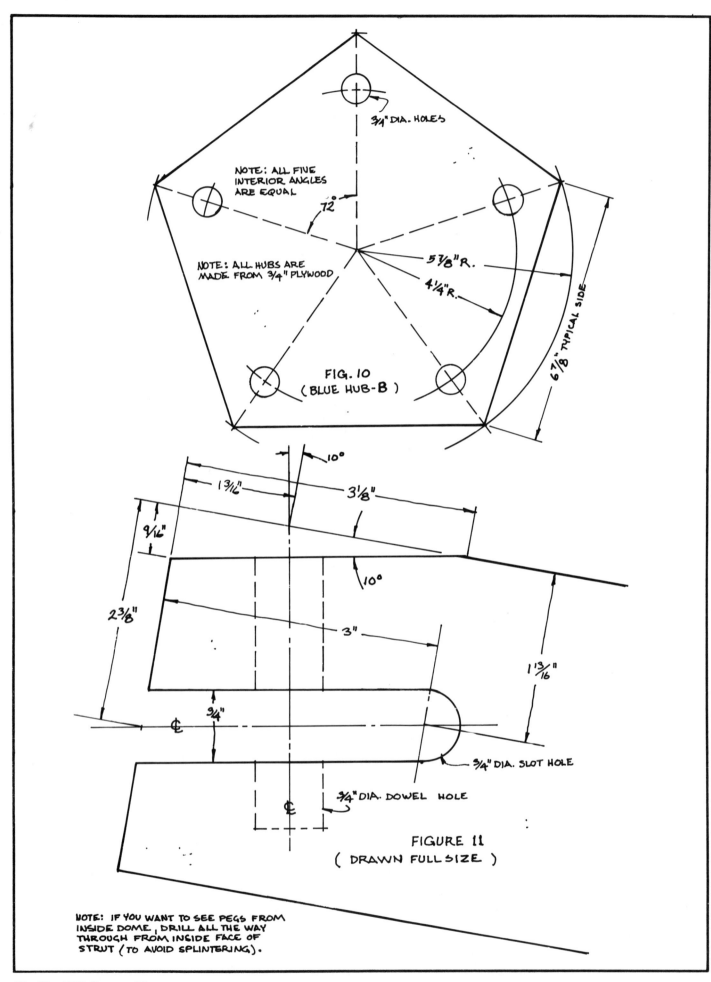

3/4" DIA. HOLES

NOTE: ALL FIVE INTERIOR ANGLES ARE EQUAL

72°

NOTE: ALL HUBS ARE MADE FROM 3/4" PLYWOOD

5 7/8" R.

4 1/4" R.

6 7/8" TYPICAL SIDE

FIG. 10
(BLUE HUB-B)

10°

1 3/16"

3 1/8"

9/16"

10°

2 3/8"

3"

1 13/16"

3/4"

¢

¢

3/4" DIA. SLOT HOLE

3/4" DIA. DOWEL HOLE

FIGURE 11
(DRAWN FULL SIZE)

NOTE: IF YOU WANT TO SEE PEGS FROM INSIDE DOME, DRILL ALL THE WAY THROUGH FROM INSIDE FACE OF STRUT (TO AVOID SPLINTERING).

To get a better idea of what the Personal Dome looks like, trace figure 12 onto a piece of paper; glue this to a piece of cardboard and make yourself a miniature dome.

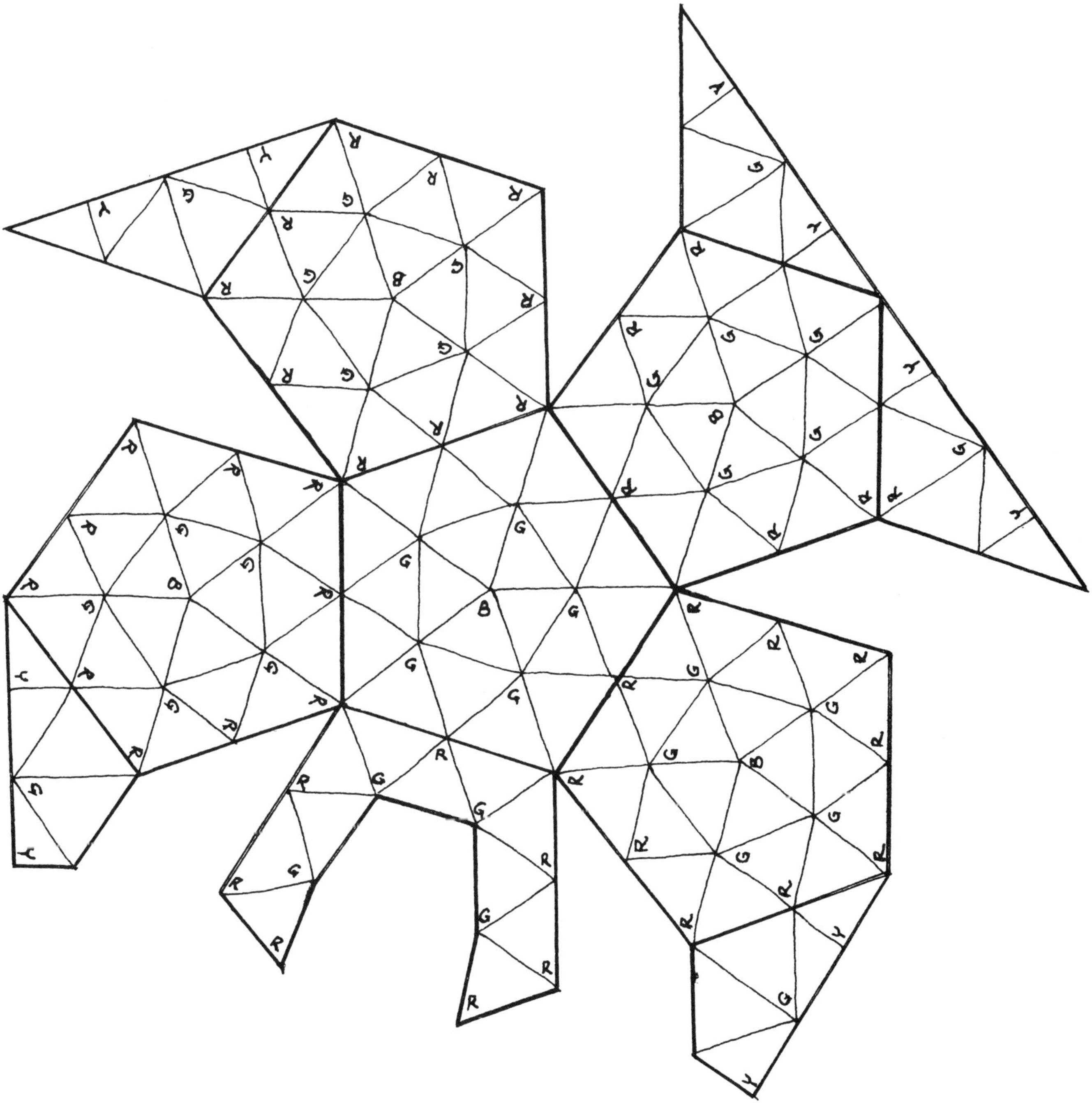

FIGURE 12

TABLE 1				
STRUT SPECIFICATIONS				
Type	Number Required	Chord Factor	Hub Centre to Hub Centre	Strut Length
BG	25	.297781R	28$\frac{9}{16}$"	22$\frac{3}{8}$"
GG	28	.346155R	33$\frac{1}{4}$"	27"
GR	103	.351623R	33$\frac{3}{4}$"	27$\frac{1}{2}$"
RR	38	.362842R	34$\frac{13}{16}$"	28$\frac{5}{8}$"
RY	10	.187601R	18$\frac{1}{8}$"	14$\frac{7}{8}$"

NOTE: RY is the odd or "truncated" strut

TABLE 2			
HUB SPECIFICATIONS			
Colour Code	Type	Number Required	Interior Angles
blue	B	5	all 72°
green	G	33	55°14'
			61°33'
			63°13'
red	R	34	all 60°

Making the Hubs

Cut plywood hubs according to the plans (figs. 8, 9, and 10). Make three master templates from the plans and then transfer the outlines of the hubs and hole centres to the plywood panels. Two 3/4-in. 4-ft. x 8-ft. panels are sufficient to make enough hubs for one dome. The G hub is to be installed directionally, meaning that the part of hub on which the holes are drilled more closely together must point towards the blue (B) hub. The R hub holes are evenly spaced and therefore have no specific directionality. The same for the blue (B) hub.

The hub, strut, and peg system (Peg-A-Strut*) has been tested to failure at five times the design load by the B.C. Tecology Centre in Vancouver, B.C.

* Registered T.M.

The Foundation

One of the basic reasons for using domes is their light weight and the fact that loads on the shell bear evenly along the whole perimeter of the dome. Consequently, very small design loads are imposed on the floor framing and the foundation. To minimize the foundation cost, a raised platform supported on posts is recommended. Here, the small dome philosophy of design demonstrates economy. Since the floor spans are short, very lightweight joists may be used. To support a 40 lbs./sq.-ft. live load, 2-in. x 6-in. joists are adequate. Or, if 2-in.-x 4-in. studs are more commonly available, an inverted T-beam may be fabricated from them.

The joists connect to ten 6 in. diameter posts, which are buried in the ground. A centre-post serves to divide the floor span so the 8-ft. joist may be used. All joists are installed radially, like the spokes of a wheel, and inter-

mediate nailing joists are installed on 2-ft. centres, which give the finished floor frame the appearance of a spider web (fig. 15).

After the foundation and floor framework have been erected, the bottom of the floor joists may be sheathed with insulating board, by nailing to the bottom of the joists. Where inverted T-beams are used, the insulating board is fitted between the radial joist and is supported by the T-flanges. The tops of the joists are covered with conventional flooring materials. This floor system may enable the space between the joists to be utilized as a return air plenum for a space-heating system.

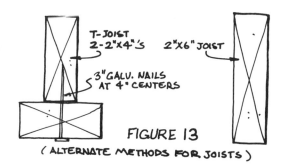

T-JOIST 2-2"X4"'S   2"X6" JOIST

3" GALV. NAILS AT 4" CENTERS

FIGURE 13

(ALTERNATE METHODS FOR JOISTS)

The plywood hubs are fastened on top of the foundation floor (fig. 16).

The dome can be assembled using the partially assembled framework itself as the scaffold. After assembly and alignment of the completed frame, the bottom hubs are securely nailed to the foundation posts (fig. 14).

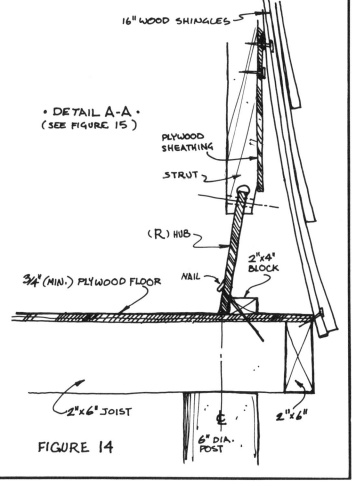

16" WOOD SHINGLES

• DETAIL A-A •
(SEE FIGURE 15)

PLYWOOD SHEATHING

STRUT

(R) HUB

3/4" (MIN.) PLYWOOD FLOOR

NAIL

2"X4" BLOCK

2"X6" JOIST

6" DIA. POST

2"X6"

FIGURE 14

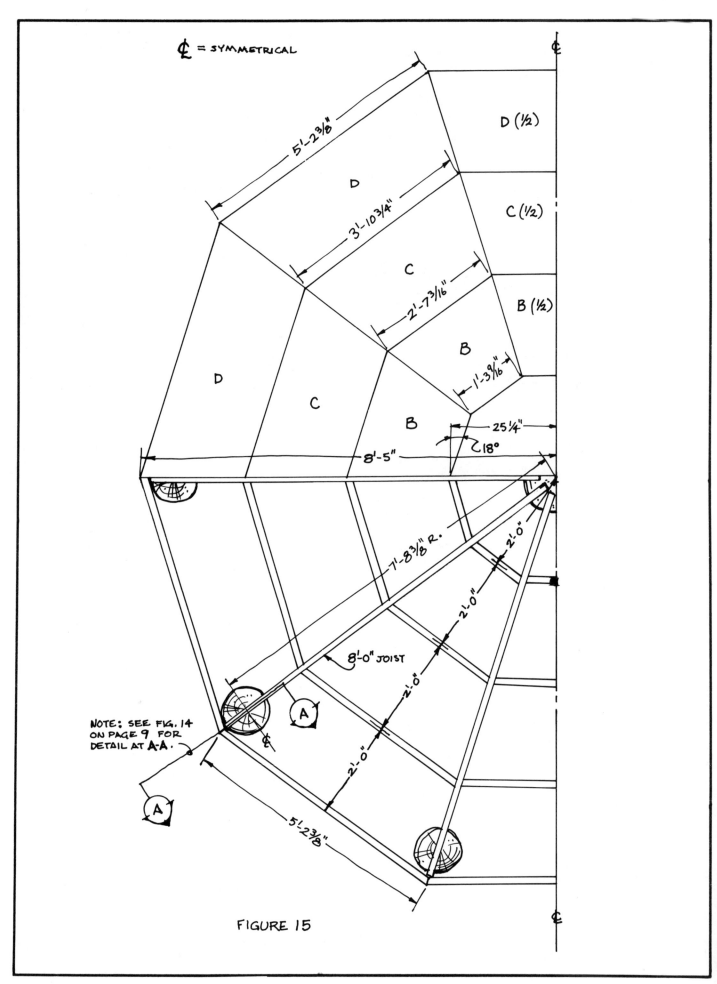

FIGURE 15

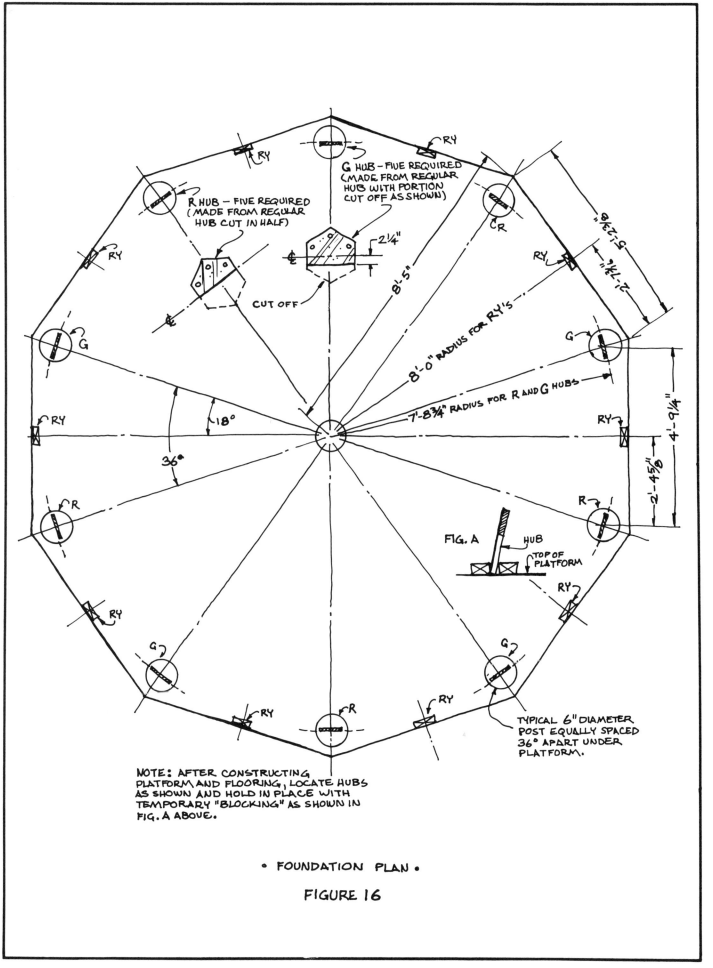

G HUB – FIVE REQUIRED (MADE FROM REGULAR HUB WITH PORTION CUT OFF AS SHOWN)

R HUB – FIVE REQUIRED (MADE FROM REGULAR HUB CUT IN HALF)

RY

CUT OFF

2¼"

8'-5"

5'-2¾"

2'-7¾"

8'-0" RADIUS FOR RY'S

7'-8¾" RADIUS FOR R AND G HUBS

18°

36°

4'-9¼"

2'-4⅝"

FIG. A   HUB

TOP OF PLATFORM

TYPICAL 6" DIAMETER POST EQUALLY SPACED 36° APART UNDER PLATFORM.

NOTE: AFTER CONSTRUCTING PLATFORM AND FLOORING, LOCATE HUBS AS SHOWN AND HOLD IN PLACE WITH TEMPORARY "BLOCKING" AS SHOWN IN FIG. A ABOVE.

• FOUNDATION PLAN •

FIGURE 16

The plywood sheathing should be cut from 4-ft. x 8-ft. sheets in a pattern similar to that illustrated in figure 17. Refer to figure 15 for the exact sizes.

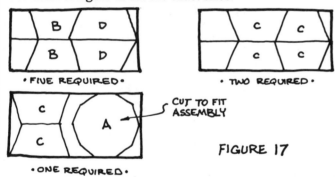

FIGURE 17

The Assembly

The struts have been colour coded (you did, didn't you?) so that they are merely put in place from the bottom hubs up. No scaffolding is needed, because the dome can be assembled with the structure itself used as the scaffold. Install the struts in a sequence with the bottom row and working upward in sort of a spiral direction. Use the folded paper model (fig. 11) as your assembly guide. To make an easy job of peg insertion, dry them out thoroughly by suspending them over coals of a wood fire or warm them at 200°F. in an oven for eight hours. This will shrink the pegs and allow them to be easily inserted. After they are in place, moisture pickup from the air will cause the dowel to expand and lock into place.

Don't plan on removing the pegs at some future date, because it won't happen. Have a picnic on top of the dome frame after driving the last peg into place. This will be your structural test. Upon completing the assembly, you may notice some hubs appear twisted. This will be due to the dome not sitting level on the foundation or you may have put some struts in the wrong place. Check this out, and if everything looks OK, twist the hubs to their correct position. This will level the dome. To check for level, place a 4-ft. carpenter's level on a straight 2 x 4 or piece of evenly-cut plywood, and align the level edge of the wood with centres of any two hubs in the row immediately above the base row. When certain that the frame is level, fasten it to the posts with dowels or drive spikes through the platform, the base hubs, and into the posts. Domes are light, and you don't want them floating away some windy night.

Sheathing (plywood or shiplap) is applied to the struts after the door and window are framed. Breather-type building paper covers the sheathing, over which is applied the finish material. Flashing is used where required. The smoke pipe and toilet vents are installed and flashed. The sheathing should be at least 5/16-in. or preferably 3/8-in. plywood. Flashing may be obtained by cutting up old auto bodies, gallon oil cans, or thin rust-proof metal. Galvanized iron or aluminum flashing may be purchased at any building supply store. The windows are then inserted, and puttied or caulked to keep out the weather.

Framing the Door

Part of the geometry is removed from the dome to facilitate placement of a door. The structural integrity is maintained by the method of framing the door. Columns are installed from the floor to the two topmost hubs. These columns take the load down to the floor, which in turn transmits the weight to the posts. This framing allows the use of an ordinary rectangular door. An old recycled door could be cut to size and installed in a frame that is also modified.

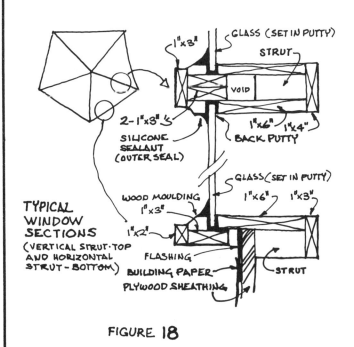

Framing the Windows

A window detail which *does* keep the rain out has been worked out and tested (fig. 18).

GLASS (SET IN PUTTY)

STRUT

1"x3"

VOID

2-1"x3"'s

SILICONE SEALANT (OUTER SEAL)

1"x6"   1"x4"

BACK PUTTY

GLASS (SET IN PUTTY)

WOOD MOULDING
1"x3"

1"x6"   1"x3"

TYPICAL WINDOW SECTIONS
(VERTICAL STRUT-TOP AND HORIZONTAL STRUT-BOTTOM)

1"x2"

FLASHING

BUILDING PAPER

PLYWOOD SHEATHING

STRUT

FIGURE 18

The structural strength of the dome does not depend upon the plywood sheathing or any other skin material for structural support. Therefore, you may install glass anywhere you prefer. However, do not remove any struts, unless you are prepared to substitute proper bracing, such as is done for the door opening. The importance of attending to details while installing window glass cannot be overemphasized, in view of the lack of conventional overhanging eaves. Use sealing compounds liberally, and only those of the highest quality.

The Sheathing Skin

As shown earlier, each pentagon is divided into five identical triangles, which are subdivided into four triangles, two of which are identical (fig. 19).

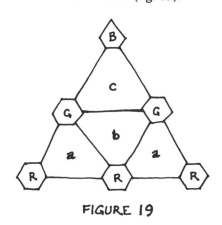

FIGURE 19

Triangles a, b, and c represent the areas to be covered by the sheathing. The templates to be made are as follows:

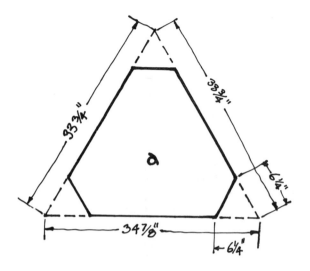

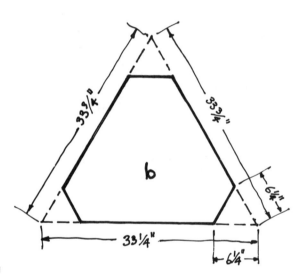

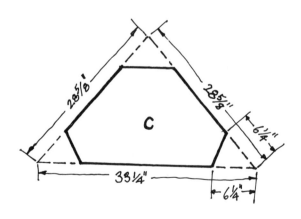

FIGURE 20

One of the reasons that we chose the 16-ft. dome with this breakdown (two frequency dodecahedron) was because it could very efficiently utilize 4-ft. x 8-ft. sheets of plywood (3/8 in. thick or more) for the skin sheathing. A cutting plan (fig. 21) has been worked out. Just for fun, cut a few triangles of different sizes out of your stock of plywood to see how everything fits—you'll feel more confident.

The alternation of a panels and b panels (fig. 21) is necessary for only seven 4-ft. x 8-ft. panels. This situation arises because 28 b's and 68 a's are required. The number of c's would be 25 or less, depending on how many windows are to be included. Along the foundation, partial panels are necessary: 10 half b's and 8 half a's.

Sheath the dome from the top down. This will allow you to use the frame as scaffolding. Sheath in a spiral pattern. The reason for this is to keep the plates (hubs) as straight as possible. The plates have a tendency to twist when stood upon, so the sheathing eliminates this problem. Maintain a constant surveillance to ensure that the hubs are not twisting. If a hub is twisted, it must be straightened or the covering material will not fit properly. Cover the sheathing with *breather-type* building paper, installing it with either staples or roofing nails. Make certain that no gaps are left and that the top section laps (by at least 8 in.) over the bottom sections. Avoid laps which end on seams in the plywood.

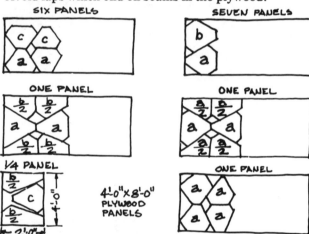

FIGURE 21

Cedar Shingle Skins

Skin designs should hopefully be of materials that are close at hand and/or are inexpensive, at the same time being waterproof and resistant to the elements. The framework is able to take the entire design load, so the skin has only to keep out the undesirable elements.

Red cedar shingles are a good solution: (a) they provide a certain degree of insulation as a result of their cell structure; (b) they are durable because of their resistance to rot; (c) they add strength to the structure and are not too difficult to install, if you follow directions.

Shingles are sold in *bundles,* four bundles making a square. A square covers approximately 100 sq. ft.. Red cedar shingles come in three lengths (16, 18, and 24 in.) and three grades (1, 2, and 3).

Exposure is the amount of shingle that is exposed to the weather. It's really important to have the right exposure or you're chancing leakage problems. The amount of exposure required is determined by the *pitch* of a roof, the pitch being the slope of a given surface. Shingles should never be less than three layers thick on a roof, and the exposure should never exceed 1/3 the length of the shingle (see table 3) for recommended exposures.

TABLE 4

Surface Segment	Area (sq. ft.)	Grade	Length	Exposure (in.)	Coverage (sq. ft.)	Quantity Shingles (squares)
(a)	285	No. 1	16	7	140	1.32
			18	8	145.5	1.27
			24	11	146.5	1.26
		No. 2	16	7	140	1.32
			18	8	145.5	1.27
			24	11	146.5	1.26
		No. 3	16	6	120	1.54
			18	6	109	1.85
			24	10	133	1.39
(b)	85	No. 1, 2 or 3	16	5	100	.85
			18	5.5	90.5	.94
			24	7.5	100	.85
(c)	87	No. 1, 2 or 3	16	3.75	75	1.16
			18	4.25	77	1.13
			24	5.75	77.8	1.12

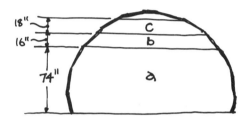

(a) treat the first 74 in., from the base to the top of the doorway, as wall, because the angle is 60° or greater.
(b) treat the next 16 in. as roof with 5 in 12 slope or greater.
(c) treat the following 18 in. as roof with less than 5 in 12 pitch.

Note: we suggest that 5d hot-dip galvanized nails be used for the entire dome to ensure adequate nail holding for the shingles.

TABLE 3

Pitch	Shingle Length (in.)	Exposure (in.)
5" in 12" or steeper	16	5
	18	5.5
	24	7.5
Greater than 3" in 12" and less than 5" in 12"	16	3.75
	18	4.25
	24	5.75
Less than 3" in 12"	Cedar shingles are not recommended	
Vertical surface 60°	Exposure should not be greater than half the shingle minus one-half inch (single course). Double course up to ¾ exposure.	

Before starting to shingle make sure that you've got *breather-type* building paper over the plywood sheathing. The bottom shingle layer should be *double* (fig. 22). Shingle from the bottom up. If you're unsure about the methods, ask any old timers in the area, because they've likely covered many a roof in their time. It's helpful to use a board tacked to the surface or a chalked line as a straight-edge to line up shingles.

Shingles provide a nice, warm, watertight surface, if you take the time and effort to use them correctly. Before use, keep them covered, if not inside. They should never be laid when they are wet. A table (table 4) of exposure and coverage for the dome has been compiled, so that you can make the best use of a given situation. The table is for use with the 16-ft. two frequency dodecahedron *only.* The 16-in. No. 3 grade shingle is the best shingle for covering this dome in terms of cost, as well as in terms of covering a curved surface. The shorter length means that there will be smaller gaps under the butts of the shingles, as a result of the angles created on the curved surface.

FIGURE 22

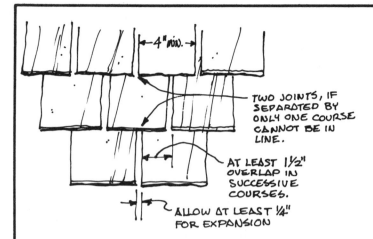

FIGURE 23

Labels in figure:
- ←4" min.→
- TWO JOINTS, IF SEPARATED BY ONLY ONE COURSE CANNOT BE IN LINE.
- AT LEAST 1½" OVERLAP IN SUCCESSIVE COURSES.
- ALLOW AT LEAST ¼" FOR EXPANSION

If there is a flat grain in the shingle, it is advisable to place it so that the bark side (side nearest the bark) is exposed. The shingle will then be less likely to become waterlogged or to turn up at the butt. Only two nails should be used per shingle.

These are nailed no more than 3/4 in. from the edges, and above the butt line of the next course (row) they should be nailed no more than 2 in. (1-1/2 in. preferably) and no less than 3/4 in. (fig. 24).

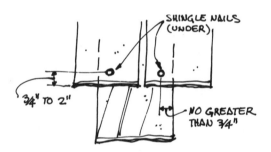

FIGURE 24

Labels in figure:
- SHINGLE NAILS (UNDER)
- ¾" TO 2"
- NO GREATER THAN ¾"

Nails should be driven flush with the surface of the shingle, but should not crush the wood (fig. 25).

THIS   NOT THIS

FIGURE 25

A study done on old shingled farm structures (in the central U.S.) found that:
(a) exposures greater than 5.5 in. contributed greatly to the number of leaks, so be conservative on your exposures.
(b) edge grain shingles significantly reduced the percentage of roofs with warped and loose shingles.
(c) more leaks occured with 16-in. shingles as opposed to 18-in. shingles.
(d) 6 in. to 8 in. in width appears to be the best, as shingles wider than 8 in. showed more warpage, breakage, and a slight increase in leaks.

Handsplit Cedar Shakes

Handsplit shakes can be made as well as installed by you do-it-yourselfers. All that is needed is a saw to cut the logs the proper length, a heavy steel blade called a "froe," and a wooden mallet of some sort. The complete process is explained on page 21.

Shakes look great and have the same good qualities as shingles; they keep the weather outside where it's supposed to be. Overlapping shakes seems to be the best way of covering a curved surface such as the Personal Dome. Table 5 shows the most optimal usage possibilities for this 16-ft. diameter dome *only*.

TABLE 5						
Surface Segment	Area (sq. ft.)	Grade (in.)	Length	Exposure (in.)	Coverage (sq. ft.)	Quantity Shakes (squares)
(a)	285	m	18	7.5	80	3.6
		n	24	10	100	2.9
(b)(c)	172	m	18	5	55	3.1
		n	24	7	70	2.5

Note: 6d nails should be adequate.

m=18" handsplit and resawn
n=24" handsplit and resawn

The 18-in. shake is the best of the commercial shakes for this dome, because the shorter length will provide for smaller gaps at the butts on the curved surface. Commercial shakes come in three lengths: 18 in., 24 in., and 32 in. Table 6 indicates the correct exposures as recommended by the Red Cedar Shingle and Handsplit Shake Bureau.

For roofs	TABLE 6		
	Maximum Exposure (in.)	For walls Max. Exposure	Best 3-ply Roof (in.)
18" shakes	8.5	8.5	5.5
24" shakes	10	11.5	7.5
32" shakes	13	15	10

Other possibilities for the skin are asphalt shingles, wire mesh and stucco, or perhaps ferro-cement. With the ferro-cement, it might even be possible to omit plywood sheathing.

Ventilation

Ventilation can be very nicely obtained by means other than installing opening windows. This is one advantage with domes, in that one can regulate the flow of air to a fine tolerance, unlike conventional dwellings. However, this is not a pure science, and one cannot provide a universal solution to ventilation problems.

You must provide means for fresh air to enter the dwelling and for used air to leave the dwelling. We may be way off base on this concept, but it appears good theory to us. Cut five vent slots about 6 in. x 18 in. in the floor, equally spaced around the perimeter. Make the slot openings adjustable by installing a sliding cover operating on a simple wooden track. These floor vents are for air intake. To provide for exhaust, or through ventilation, erect a cupola on top of the dome, beginning from the hubs surrounding the centre pentagonal hub. Do not remove any struts, or the dome will be substantially weakened. Install five vents of equal area to those in the floor. The top of the cupola may be shingled, or domed with clear plastic or glass and used for penta-star gazing. Whatever you do, be liberal with the caulking compound. The cupola also serves to shed rain which might work under rooftop shingles lying almost parallel to the ground, thus inviting sister rain to enter. Screen all vents, both

intake and exhaust. We hope that necessity will enable you to arrive at simpler solutions than those we have come up with.

Heating and Insulation

Any kind of wood burning stove is OK for heating. You can insulate between the struts with fibreglass batting, which comes equipped with aluminum foil pasted to one side. Cut the insulation, which comes in 24-in. rolls, into triangles which are slightly larger than the dome triangles. Then, when you push the cut insulation into the openings between struts (with the aluminum side towards the inside of the dome), friction will hold the insulation in place.

Two inches of fibreglass will suit the requirements for heating insulation in areas where up to 8,000 degree-days* are encountered. For up to 12,000 degree-days, 3 in. of fibreglass is required.

When installing the chimney for the stove, remember that the chimney pipe can get red hot. If you don't insulate the pipe from the dome structure, you stand a good chance of having your hard-earned labours go up in smoke. Any hardware store should have the insulating "thimble" and roof flashing which is required to afford protection and assure a watertight seal around the pipe.

To avoid downdrafts, the chimney pipe should extend 3 ft. above the roof surface or structure within a horizontal distance of 10 ft. from the chimney. This means that you should make the chimney so that it extends 2 ft. above the highest point of the dome, which includes the cupola, should you have one.

Lining the Inside of the Dome

Gyprock (drywall) 3/8 in. thick is cheap and easy to work with. It is also fire resistant. Natural material can be used as well: cedar planks, burlap, used weathered planks, driftwood, woven reeds, and bulrushes. Just keep the combustible areas away from the stove by at least 4 ft.

*Each degree that the mean daily temperature is below 65°F. is a degree day.

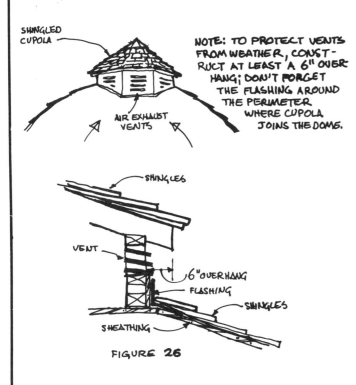

FIGURE 26

TABLE 7 MATERIALS LIST		
Material	Type	Quantity
2'' x 4'' fir, spruce, or cedar	economy grade or better	550 lineal feet
4' x 8' x ¼'' exterior plywood	waterproof sheathing grade	2 panels
2'' x 4'' or 2'' x 6'' fir for T-beams	no. 3 grade	20 pcs.. 7'10'' to 8' and 50' random length
4' x 8' x ⅜'' exterior plywood	waterproof sheathing grade	18 panels
2'' x 4'' fir or cedar	economy grade or better	100 lineal feet in random lengths
6'' diameter cedar		11 posts
¼'' diameter doweling	fir or hardwood	40 lineal feet
roofing paper	asphalt impregnated breather-type	5 - 100' rolls
shingles	refer to tables as required	
insulation		

Splitting Shakes

The varieties of timber adapted to making shakes are few. The wood should split easily and true; when exposed to the weather on the building, it should not warp from its place or "curl" up. The durability of the timber is a secondary consideration—shakes wear out more than they rot—and the varieties which would be least subject to these changes might not, for good reasons, be at all suitable for roofing purposes. Pine is doubtless the best, but hemlock, cedar, and chestnut are excellent. The trees should not have passed their prime when cut, but should be vigorous in growth and sound at the heart, so that the wood will not be "brash."

The first work to be done when we commence shake making is to get out the bolts. Saw the trunk of the tree with a cross-cut saw into sections, each one of the length you intend to make the shingles. Sixteen inches is sufficient length for any easy splitting wood, and if it be tough or "brashy," twelve will do. The shorter the shingles, the less space you can lay to the weather, and the more time and nails it will take to make them into a roof. These sections of the trunk may then be set on end and split into bolts.

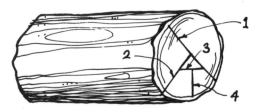

The numbered lines in the drawing show the place and order in which the section should be split. Line 1 divides it through the centre; line 2 quarters it; line 3 takes off the heart block; and line 4 finishes the shingle bolts. If the tree is large, however, so that these bolts are wider than it is practicable to make the shakes, they can be further subdivided. The splitting may be done rapidly with the axe and a light maul, drawing the axe first carefully along the longest lines, and tapping it lightly with the maul, until the block is "checked," when a blow or two on the axe placed in the centre will open it as desired. The bark should next be removed from the bolts, and they should be piled under cover so that the sun and wind will not "season check" them.

Having the bolts in the shop, next proceed to split them into rough shakes with the mallet and froe.

Splitting the Bolts

The figure shows the proper way of splitting a bolt. First, split it at line A; this should take off a piece thick enough for four shingles. Next divide this piece through the centre, as shown by line B; the pieces are then wide enough for two shakes. These are split through the middle, which finishes them. If you undertake to split off each shake separately from the side of the bolt, you will almost invariably "run out," and the timber be wasted.

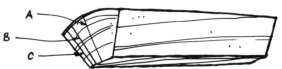

A large-sized shaving-knife and a shaving horse or bench are necessary to shave and complete the shakes.

The froe is formed of a heavy steel blade, eight or ten inches long and two wide, having a dull edge; the handle is a foot long, and projects from one end of the blade at right angles to it. When the blade is driven into the bolt and partially splits it, the handle can be forced over to one side with the hand or by a blow from the mallet, and the leverage force thus exerted splits off the shake. In this operation, skill and practice in the art come most into use. If the check or split runs out, the shake will be too short, and therefore worthless, and the timber wasted. The operator must change his block, end for end, as circumstances require, and work carefully. Three-eighths of an inch is the proper thickness for the shakes.

Shaving Bench and Knife

Shave the butt-end of the shake first; this will require but a stroke or two, since it is already of the desired thickness if properly split. Next, edge the shake on the right or left hand side, as most convenient, taking off, when you meet it, all of the sap wood. Change ends of the shake, shave both sides, thinning it gradually from the butt-end to the top, straightening the other edge, and it is finished. A smart workman will split out and shave one thousand in a day.

The shakes should be packed away in tiers, lapping them as in the common bunches which you see for sale, and a plank put on the top of the pile and weighted down, so as to keep them in proper shape until seasoned.

Pit Privies

by Vic Marks

Pit privies have proved themselves useful for quite a few centuries and, having changed little in such a long time, still have a lot to offer us hardy souls who find them preferable to the septic tank. There are two types of pit privies: those that don't recycle the wastes and those that do. The types that don't recycle the wastes are the most common, but not necessarily the best.

A Healthy Privy

There is no rule which you can apply to determine how far the privy must be from your water source. The privy should be located downhill from any wells or streams. This lessens the possibility of bacterial pollution to your drinking water. A level place is acceptable and, if you *must* put it uphill from the water source, place it at least 100 ft. from the well or stream. Fifty feet is the minimum distance under favourable conditions.

Another factor to be aware of is the depth of your well. In homogeneous soil (uniformly structured), your chance of ground-water pollution is virtually nil if the bottom of the pit is 5 ft. above the ground-water table. But be careful in areas containing fissured rocks or limestone formations, since pollution may be carried directly through solution channels and without natural filtration to distant wells or other sources of drinking-water supplies.

The Pit

The pit acts as both a storehouse and isolation chamber for all germs connected with human wastes.

The standard privy should last anywhere from 4 to 15 years (see table below) without being filled up, depending on how deep the pit is and how many people are using it. A decomposition process takes place in the pit which decreases the volume of wastes deposited by about 50 per cent. It's been found that each person leaves a legacy of about 3 cu. ft. of excreta each year.

PIT VOLUME AND DEPTH* FOR A PRIVY WITH AN AREA OF 9 SQUARE FEET TO BE USED BY 5 PEOPLE		
Service Life	Depth (ft.)	Volume (cu. ft.)
4 Years	6.7	60
8 years	13.3	120

*Depth given is effective pit depth, and 1 to 2 feet are usually added to obtain overall depth of pit.

Privy Size

A 3-ft.-sq. pit is the normal size, although there is no standardized pit size. If you're in an area where the pit might cave in, *line it*. Even in solid soil it's a good idea to line the top two feet of the pit to prevent caving in from the weight of the floor and superstructure. Try to use whatever natural materials are around for this purpose (integrate the outhouse into the environment); stone, roughhewn logs, home-made bricks, lumber, or concrete blocks. Try to find some recycled material to suit the purpose.

The Base

The base serves as a solid foundation upon which the floor can rest. It helps to prevent the exit of hookworm larvae and other crawlies which snap at your arse. Properly made, of hard durable material, it also helps to prevent the entrance of burrowing rodents and of surface water into the pit. The foundation should be at least 4 in. wide on top in order to provide a stable contact with the ground. If it's located where there's a possibility of flooding, the base should be at least 6 in. high. (A mound of dirt approximately 2 ft. high should also encircle the privy.) The base can be made of plain or reinforced precast cement (see illustrations), soil cement (5 to 6 per cent mixed with sandy clay soil), clay bricks, stone masonry, or rough-cut logs (preferably hardwood).

A Hewn Log Privy Base

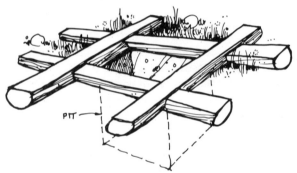

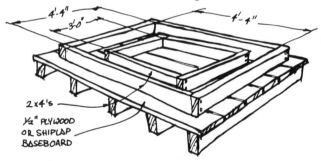

Build a wooden form in which you can pour a concrete ring sill that is 4 in. thick, with outside dimensions of 4 ft. 4 in. x 4 ft. 4 in., and with a hole in its centre measuring 3 ft. x 3 ft. Pour the ring sill.

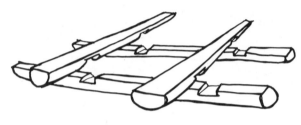

•WOODEN FORM FOR RING SILL•

Next, build another form in which to pour a slab of concrete 3 ft. 8 in. square (2-1/2 to 3 in. thick), having a hole in its centre to suit your own design. A wooden riser box with cover will have to be constructed and mounted on the slab later.

All concrete should be suitably reinforced with steel rods, and with eye and anchor bolts embedded in the sill and slab.

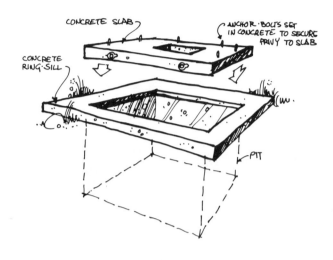

The Floor

The floor should fit tightly to the base, with a minimum of small cracks and openings between base and floor. Concrete is preferable, but wood is ok if you fit the boards tightly together or use the type with a tongue and groove.

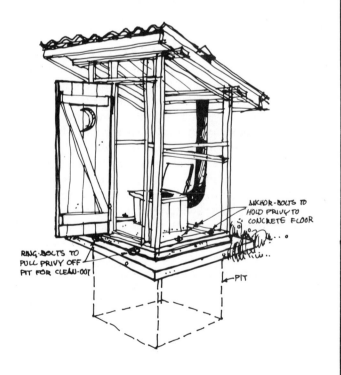

The House

The house should fit the dimensions of the floor or slab. You should keep in mind the fact that when the pit fills, you're going to have to move the house (or construct another house, which is somewhat of a waste). So try to make it strong and flexible enough to be moved; this is especially important if you have a compost privy.

It's a good idea to make openings 4 to 6 in. wide at the top of the walls to allow proper ventilation.

It's always nice to have lots of light in the outhouse, but you should always provide enough shade over an uncovered seat or hole in order not to attract flies.

A good habit to get into, if you have a wood burning stove, is to add some ashes occasionally to keep the smells down. If you're bothered by mosquitoes breeding in the pit, pour a cup of kerosene down the hole once a week.

The provision of a pit or seat vent is a good idea. There is sometimes quite a difference in temperature between the air in the pit and the outside air. This temperature difference causes condensation on the under side of the seat cover. It's also believed that a vent induces a draught of air which helps to keep the pit materials dry and small in bulk.

The Compost Privy

The use of human wastes as a compost material has been practiced in China for centuries. There is no reason why it can't be done in North America.

The composting is extremely important. Never use excrement raw for fertilization. The high temperature created by decomposition is necessary to destroy bacteria and worm eggs.

The privy pit, slab, location, and other features need be no different from those previously described. However, the compost privy should be provided with the largest possible capacity so that it will not fill too fast. For this reason, you might want to enlarge the pit. Do this by doubling the length of the pit, therefore having part of the vault outside the house, but covered with a tight-fitting and durable cover.

The composting method is based on anaerobic decomposition of organic wastes, which are left undisturbed during a period of at least six months to ensure destruction of pathogen and ova of helminths. The best procedure is:

(1) Dig a pit, making sure that the bottom of it is above ground-water level: don't take chances of polluting drinking water.

(2) Before the slab is put in place, cover the bottom 20 in. of the pit with grass cuttings, fine leaves, garbage, paper, etc.; but don't allow rubbish such as metal cans, glass bottles, or other non-organic matter.

(3) Place the slab, and build the house, keeping in mind that they will both be moved periodically to other sites.

(4) In addition to depositing human wastes, throw the daily organic garbage into the pit, along with cow, horse sheep, chicken, or pig manure, as well as urine-soaked earth or straw. The latter materials are important, as urine is rich in nitrogen, an essential plant nutrient.

(5) About once a week, throw about five pounds of grass

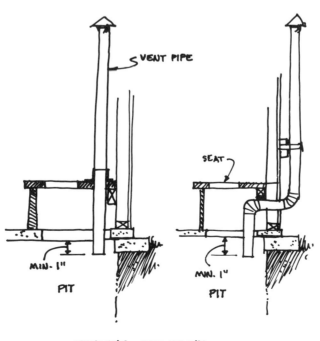

• VENTING PIT PRIVY •

clippings and fine-textured leaves into the pit. If you don't have grass clippings but have access to seaweed, use it instead. It will require a bit of experimentation to get the optimal fertilizer, so use whatever materials are available. Refer to Rodale's *Encyclopedia of Organic Gardening or Composting* for composting mixtures.

(6) When the pit's contents reach a level of 20 in. below ground, dig a new pit 5 to 6 ft. away (more if desired), and move the house and slab over it. Level the first pit with 6 in. of grass clippings and leaves, and the top 14 in. with well-tamped earth.

(7) When the second pit is filled in the same manner, uncover the first pit and remove the compost. It should be stable, and will provide a good fertilizer which can be applied immediately to the fields or stored.

The size of the pit depends on your needs for fertilizer and the number of people using the privy. The proportion of excrement that can be added to refuse for satisfactory composting *should* be about one to five by volume. From the table (p. 22) it can be seen that a family of five will produce 60 cu. ft. of partly digested excrement in four years. Therefore, 1/5 of a pit of 60 cu. ft. capacity would be filled in approximately 9 to 10 months, which is a good cycle for a compost privy.

Rather than build two pits and move the structure back and forth, you might want to build a double privy or double "vault" privy. This consists of a large vault divided into two compartments, each of which is topped by a slab and a hole. The house is likewise partitioned into two houses with separate entrances. In practice, the vaults are filled and emptied alternately in the same manner as previously described. But people, being what they are, tend to use both privies, so if you're going to use this method get a padlock for the one not in use.

Bibliography

Excreta Disposal for Rural Areas and Small Communities,
E.G. Wagner and J.N. Lanoix
World Health Organization
United Nations
New York, N.Y.

Village Technology Handbook
VITA
College Campus
Schenectady, N.Y.

The Mother Earth News
TMEN Inc.
P.O. Box 38
Madison, Ohio

Little Extras that Make Privies more Pleasurable

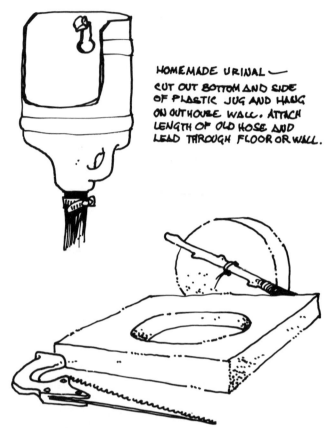

HOMEMADE URINAL — CUT OUT BOTTOM AND SIDE OF PLASTIC JUG AND HANG ON OUTHOUSE WALL. ATTACH LENGTH OF OLD HOSE AND LEAD THROUGH FLOOR OR WALL.

WARM SEAT — ON THOSE COLD, WINTRY DAYS (OR WORSE, NIGHTS) A SECTION OF STYROFOAM WITH A HOLE CUT IN THE CENTRE WILL WARM UP WHEN YOU SIT ON IT! CUT THE HOLE WITH A KEYHOLE SAW OR HACKSAW BLADE AND YOU CAN USE THE CENTRE PIECE FOR A LID.

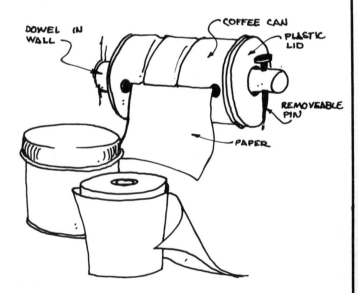

DOWEL IN WALL
COFFEE CAN
PLASTIC LID
REMOVEABLE PIN
PAPER

TOILET-PAPER CONTAINERS — TOBACCO TINS OR COFFEE CANS MAKE GOOD PROTECTION AGAINST DAMP OR ANIMALS.

How to Store Your Fruits & Vegetables

by Vic Marks

A lot of people, both country and city folk, are growing their own vegetables and fruits. With each passing season, the composted and mulched gardens are producing more abundant crops and, as the crops increase, so does the desire to eat healthy organically-grown produce all year round. A storage cellar of some sort is a vital necessity to anybody who lacks either the climate or a greenhouse to ensure fresh vegetables at all times of the year, and wishes to enjoy home-grown produce during those long wintry months.*

Vegetable Classes

Vegetables fall into three classes or groups, determined by their perishableness:

(1) The *quickly perishable:* green peas, green limas, corn, asparagus; green vegetables such as spinach, chard, and lettuce.

(2) The *perishables:* broccoli, cauliflower, late cabbage, and onions.

(3) The *keepers:* potatoes, turnips, beets, carrots, and similar root crops; as well as pumpkins, late squash, and celery.

These classes aren't sharply divided, so look at table 1 to find the approximate lifespan of each.

Store only sound vegetables of good quality. Can or eat in the fall any that don't look too healthy. If they rot in the shelter and you don't happen to notice, you'll lose a

* The cellars, pits, and outbuildings described in this article are practical only where the outside temperatures during winter average 30 F. or below.

good part of your winter food stash. Harvesting should be delayed as long as possible without danger of freezing.

Handle everything with care to avoid cuts and bruises, especially if you wash the vegetables. Let excess water evaporate before storing.

Successful Fruit Storage

How well your fruits are going to keep in storage depends on:

(1) The quality of the produce. The fruits should be without decay, disease, insects, and bruises caused by handling. One bad (i.e., rotten or bruised) apple can destroy the lot.

(2) Storing the right varieties. Ones that mature late are the best.

(3) Harvesting at proper time (refer to preparation section).

(4) Keeping the right temperature and humidity in the storage room (refer to storage conditions section).

(5) The temperature and humidity of the storage space.

Placing fruits and vegetables in storage, before cold weather starts in the fall, is a frequent cause of early spoilage. One of the most difficult steps in sorting your produce is to keep it in prime condition from the time of maturity until the night temperature is low enough to cool the storage area. If *possible,* store fruits in a different storage space from the vegetables, because odours and undesirable flavours can be picked up from the strong-smelling ones such as potatoes, turnips, and cabbage.

Proper Storage Temperatures and Humidity

The humidity and temperature requirements of produce vary greatly, some requiring warm dry conditions (sweet potatoes, tomatoes) and others cold moist conditions (cabbage, apples, root crops). Refer to table 1 to determine the best conditions.

Without proper moisture (humidity), stored vegetables and fruits shrivel, lose quality, and eventually become too god awful to eat. Two common methods used to maintain the proper humidity are:

(1) The use of water to raise the humidity of the storage air.

(2) The use of ventilated polyethylene or cellophane bags and box liners.

The first method is accomplished by frequently sprinkling the floor with water, or by placing large pans of water under fresh-air intake vents (not as effective), or by covering the floor with wet materials such as straw, sawdust, or a combination of these. However, these methods won't stop the root crops from shriveling up on you. The best way to stop root crops from shriveling is to put them in polyethylene bags or box liners, *but* polyethylene is virtually indestructible, non-biodegradable, and possibly passes cancer along in foods that are stored in them for long periods of time. Use cellophane bags instead. Cut a few 1/2 to 3/8 inch holes in the sides of the bags, stuff them full of produce, tie the tops (don't seal them), and prepare yourself for some mighty fine winter eating.

As far as temperature is concerned, get at least two good thermometers (preferably the kind that record minimum and maximum temperatures), placing one in the coldest spot in your storage room and the other one outdoors.

You'll probably find that it's necessary to daily regulate the temperature by opening or closing the ventilators. If temperatures consistently drop below 0°F., you may have to install a small heater of some sort. If you have electricity, a small 600-watt heater with a thermostat will suffice.

Plant late all that will be stored. This way you'll be able to solve the problem of how to keep the produce from rotting before the weather gets cool enough to keep the storage room cold. See that the vegetables and fruits are as cool as possible when you put them in storage. Harvest early in the morning, or let the crops cool outdoors overnight before storing them—and don't bother waxing anything, because it just doesn't help.

Dried beans and peas (including lima and soy beans) can easily be stored, as long as you make a few preparatory steps. First, dry the beans in one of two ways:

(1) Pick the pods as soon as they mature and spread them in a warm dry place until they are thoroughly dry, or

(2) Pull and dry the bean plants like hay, after most of the pods are ripe.

After drying the beans, shell them, and either refrigerate them at 0°F. or below for three or four days, or heat them in an oven at 135°F. for 30 to 60 minutes, in order to protect them from destruction by moths or weevils.

Head lettuce, leeks, and *endive* can be footed in dirt in the storage cellar, watered occasionally, and sometimes kept until Christmas or later. Root crops such as cauliflower and brussel sprouts can be handled in the same fashion.

Root crops such as carrots, turnips, beets, parsnips, chard, rutabagas, etc. shouldn't be harvested until late fall (November). Leave them in the ground as long as possible, as light frosts won't hurt them. Dig your root crops when the ground is dry, and cut the tops off about an inch above the root. Don't wash them. You'll find that root crops will keep fresher when bedded in layers of moist sand, peat, or sphagnum moss, or packed in boxes (or cans) surrounded by straw. Cellophane or polyethylene bags can also be used.

Kohlrabi can be stored after removal of leaves and roots. An area of high moisture (95 per cent humidity) and low temperature (32° to 34°F.) is best.

Parsnips, salsify, Jerusalem artichokes, and often *carrots* can be left in the ground throughout the winter. To make digging easier, cover the rows with about one foot of leaves or straw before the ground has frozen.

Onions must be cured. Leave them (after pulling) on the ground for at least two to three days, then place them in crates in an open shed (or somewhere similar) for several weeks to complete curing. Remove the tops and store them in bins or stringbags in a dry, well-ventilated place, such as an attic or unheated room. Light freezing won't hurt onions, as long as you don't handle them while they are frozen.

Late potatoes are much easier to store than early varieties, mainly because you can leave them in the ground until the cool temperatures are around. For several months after harvesting they can be held in almost any storage location, as this is their normal resting period, but they *must* be stored in the dark. After this period, temperatures between 34° and 41°F. are necessary to prevent sprouting, so as soon as temperatures permit, put them in the storage area. If you find the potatoes are a little sweet tasting after a couple of months of storage (low temperatures turn starch into sugar), let them sit in your kitchen cupboard (or some equally warm place) for a week before you use them. *Never* store potatoes with apples, as flavours will mix.

Sweet potatoes should be free from injury, and need to be cured (see early potatoes) before final storage. Lots of air circulation and high temperatures over a period of 10 days to 3 weeks are necessary. After curing, sweet potatoes should be placed in a warm (50° to 60°F.) room.

Early potatoes are usually harvested when temperatures are high, so you have to take precautions if you want them to keep. After harvesting (early morning is best), cure the potatoes by storing them in moist air for 10 days to 3 weeks where the temperature is between 60° to 75°F. Lots of air circulation is important. The curing eliminates excess water and heals skinned areas and cracks. This helps to prevent decay, but isn't altogether

TABLE 1
FRUIT AND VEGETABLE STORAGE

Commodity	Freezing point	Place to Store	Storage Conditions		Length of storage period
	°F.		Temperature °F.	Humidity	
Vegetables:					
Dry beans and peas	---	Any cool, dry place		Dry	As long as desired
Late cabbage	30.4	Pit, trench, or outdoor cellar	Near 32° as possible	Moderately moist	Through late fall and winter
Cauliflower	30.3	Storage cellar	" "	" "	6 to 8 weeks
Late celery	31.6	Pit or trench; roots in soil in storage cellar.	" "	" "	Through late fall and winter
Endive	31.9	Roots in soil in storage cellar	" "	" "	2 to 3 months
Onions	30.6	Any cool, dry place	" "	Dry	Through fall and winter
Parsnips	30.4	Where they grew, or in storage cellar.	" "	Moist	" " ; " "
Peppers	30.7	Unheated basement or room	45° to 50°	Moderately moist	2 to 3 weeks
Potatoes	30.9	Pit or in storage cellar	35° to 40°	"	Through fall and winter,
Pumpkins and squashes	30.5	Home cellar or basement	55°	Moderately dry	" " ; " "
Root crops (miscellaneous)	---	Pit or in storage cellar	Near 32° as possible	Moist	" " ; " "
Sweet potatoes	29.7	Home cellar or basement	55° to 60°	Moderately dry	" " ; " "
Tomatoes (mature green)	31.0	" " "	55° to 70°	"	4 to 6 weeks
Fruits:					
Apples	29.0	Fruit storage cellar	Near 32° as possible	Moderately moist	Through fall and winter
Grapefruit	29.8	" "	" "	"	4 to 6 weeks
Grapes	28.1	" "	" "	"	1 to 2 months
Oranges	30.5	" "	" "	"	4 to 6 weeks
Pears	29.2	" "	" "	"	2 to 5 months

necessary for early potatoes. Decay is not likely to be a problem if you store them at 70° to 75°F. . If your summers are mild, just bank (or ridge) some soil around the potato plants in the late summer, thus protecting them from light (turns them green and inedible) and providing for drainage till you dig them in the fall—but don't leave potatoes undug if your region gets high temperatures and heavy rainfall.

Celery is best maintained by pulling the crop. Leave the tops dry: do not wash them. The roots should be placed in slightly moist sand or soil. To avoid odour contamination, do not store with cabbage or turnips.

Another method of storing celery is to dig a trench 10 to 12 inches wide, about 24 inches deep, and any desired length. Dig the plants when they are fully grown, taking a clump of soil with the roots. Then pack the plants in the trench, watering them as you do so, and leave the trench open long enough for the plant tops to dry off. You won't have to water them again, unless the soil is very dry at the time of storing or extended warm weather follows it. Make a sloping roof for the trench by setting a 12-inch board on edge beside the trench; bank soil against the board and then put boards, poles, cornstalks (which have had the tops removed) across the trench, with one end resting on the upright board and the other end on the ground. Spread a light covering of straw or other material that will pack closely over the roof. As the weather becomes colder, add more covering.

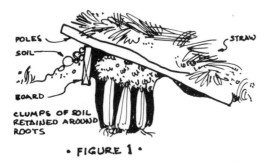

· FIGURE 1 ·

You can also store celery in a hotbed. First remove surplus soil from the hotbed and substitute a covering of boards for the sash. Then pack the celery in the hotbed in the same way you would pack them in a trench.

Yet another method of celery storage is to bank a few inches of soil around the base of the plants in the garden at the end of the growing season. Build the bank up to the top of the plants before severe freezing occurs and, as weather becomes colder, cover the banking with straw or corn fodder held in place with boards.

Cabbage and *Chinese cabbage* may be stored in outdoor storage cellars, in cone-shaped pits, or in long pits (fig. 2). Pits seem preferable, because of odour contamination to other produce from cabbage. The advantage of long pits over cone-shaped pits is that you can remove a few heads of cabbage from a long pit without disturbing the rest of the pit. To store cabbages in a long pit, pull the plants out by the roots, place them head down in the pit, and cover them with soil.

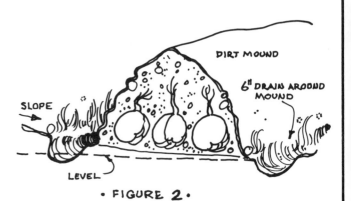

· FIGURE 2 ·

You can also store cabbage as illustrated in figure 3. Pull the plants out by the roots and set them side by side with their roots in the trench. Pack soil around the roots and then build a frame about two feet high around the trench. The frame may be made of boards, poles, or stakes driven in the ground. Next, bank soil around the frame. Finally, place poles across the tip of the frame to hold a covering of straw, hay, or corn fodder.

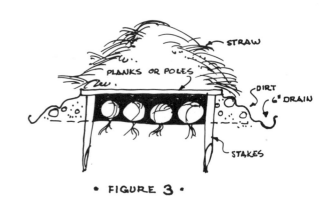

· FIGURE 3 ·

For cellar storage, first remove the outer loose leaves. Remove the roots and stem, and wrap the cabbages. Put them in boxes and bins and place them in your storage cellar.

Many people store root crops right in the ground where they grew. To do this, mulch the roots in early fall to prevent alternate freezing and thawing. When the weather is always cold, pull back the mulch and allow the roots to become thoroughly frozen. Then mulch them heavily. The roots are dug as needed. This is especially handy in light snow districts.

Root crops keep best between 32° and 40°F. Continued storage above 40°F. causes them to sprout new tops and to become woody. Watch out for turnips and rutabagas, as they give off odours; the best place for them is an outdoor cellar or pit. A cone-shaped pit (fig. 4) is a good place for root crops but only in areas where they are protected from freezing.

Pumpkins and *squashes* should be harvested before frost and left with a small piece of stem on them when they are cut from the plants. If possible, cure them for 10 days at 80° to 85°F., and if these temperatures are impossible to maintain, just leave them beside your furnace for at least two weeks. Curing will harden the rinds and heal surface cuts, but won't help bruised areas and pickleworm injuries. Don't store pumpkins or squashes below 50°F. (except for acorn squashes, which shouldn't be cured and are best stored between 45° to 50°F.).

Tomatoes should be picked from healthy vines late in the fall, which means planting in the spring. Harvest tomatoes before the first frost (when the temperatures start to range between 32° and 50°F.) or if the frost gets them first, pick the ones not damaged by freezing. After picking and stemming the tomatoes, wash and dry them before storing. Wiping them isn't a good idea, as it causes scarring which leads to decay. Store tomatoes that show red separately from green tomatoes, as this will reduce bruising and separate the tomatoes that will be used first. Pack the green tomatoes one or two layers deep in shallow boxes or trays for ripening. At 55°F. mature green tomatoes will take about 25 to 28 days to ripen, and should be wrapped (use paper or cellophane) if your storage area is dry. Do not put them in an area with temperatures below 50°F. Sort the tomatoes every 7 to 10 days, separating the reds from the greens, and removing any that show decay.

With *sunflowers,* cut off the heads with a foot of stalk attached when the birds are beginning to eat ripe outer rows of seeds. Hang them in a cool, dry place to dry; the seeds in the centre rows, which are still green, will ripen. When all the seeds are ripe and dry, remove seeds by rubbing lightly. Store your seeds in dry, airtight containers.

Garlic should be stored by braiding the stems together and hanging in a shed, garage, or basement.

Apples should be picked when they are mature, but still hard. In picking, the apples should be lifted up and away from the branch so that the stem comes away with the apple. When the stem is jerked out, the centre of the apple starts to decay. If you pick them when they are still green, they are subject to scald and bitter-pit. Overmature apples will quickly ripen on you. Bruising and skin cuts not only make the fruit more subject to decay, but actually make it deteriorate faster in storage. Do not store apples that have glassy spots in the flesh. This is known as water core. Varieties that are highly subject to scald should be mixed with shredded oiled paper at the rate of one-half pound of paper per bushel, or else wrapped with oiled paper. Another method which might extend apple storage life is to dip them in a mixture of water and concentrated kelp juice.

Varieties that mature in September (i.e. Grimes Golden, Jonathan) cannot be kept long. Athan, McIntosh, Cortland, and Delicious (red and golden) last for two to five months. Stayman, Winesap, Northern Spy, York Imperial, Arkansas Black Twig, Baldwin, Ben-Davis, and Rome Beauty will store four to six months. The Winesap and Yellow frequently last from five to

*Yellow Newton, Rhode Island Greening and McIntosh are better when stored at 36° to 38°F.

eight months. You can store apples many ways, as long as you don't allow them to freeze (see table 1 for freezing points). When the days and nights are cold, apples should be stored in insulated boxes in outbuildings, in hay in a barn, in straw-lined pits, or in soil and straw-covered barrels. These methods *won't* protect apples against freezing if the temperatures are below 10°F.

Pears should be harvested when they still seem to be immature. If allowed to begin to yellow on the tree, they develop hard gritty cells in the flesh. They are best picked in the same manner as apples. Winter Nelis, Anjou, and Easter Buerre store the best (up to seven months). You'll have to allow them to ripen at room temperature after you take them out of storage.

Growing organic *grain* is a satisfying operation, but improper storage can lose all the advantages inherent in the process. The old-time farmer used to cut and bind grain in sheaves, where it stood and cured gradually in the fields before being threshed. Today's mechanized methods save time, but have certain disadvantages. When grain is harvested by combine, it is cut, hulled, and poured into 100-pound bags, but it is still "green" and must be treated with care to prevent mold. It may seem dry, but it will continue to give off moisture for over a month. Furthermore, wild garlic, ragweed, and other seeds will be included in each bag. The grain must be cleaned with a fan seed cleaner, or winnowed outdoors by throwing it up in a breeze, or dropping it past a fan to blow away chaff. Once cleaned, bags should be placed on end on slats in a dry place (not on a dirt or concrete floor), and separated by several inches to allow air circulation. The presence of a good cat will prevent mouse damage; otherwise, use a metal, screened enclosure.

After a few days, invert the bags and disturb the grain to permit air to reach all kernels. Invert again each week for about a month, after which time the grain should be cured. The most logical method for storage after curing is a metal drum in a dry place. Temperatures between 40° and 50°F. with little moisture (50 per cent humidity) seem to be the best. Small quantities can be stored in glass jars, and, if you have a freezer, you can keep wheat indefinitely.

If your grain becomes mouldy from accidental exposure to moisture, it may not be a complete loss. Just wash it in plain lukewarm water several times and dry over a hot-air furnace grate or similar source of warmth. You can tell from the smell whether it is still musty or not.

Seeds should be stored where there are fairly cool temperatures maintained, as well as low moisture (humidity).

Pit-type Methods of Storage

If you have neither the energy nor the money to build a permanent storage room, mound or pit storage is the cheapest and easiest alternative. They are mainly used to store potatoes, carrots, beets, turnips, salsify, parsnips, cabbage, and even fruits such as apples and pears. The pit may be built on the ground, or in a hole six to eight inches deep in a well-drained location. After picking a spot, cover it with a layer of straw, leaves, or other bedding material. Next, stack the vegetables or fruits on the bedding in a cone-shaped pile. Cover the produce with more bedding, and then cover the entire pile with three or four inches of soil. Firm the soil with the back of a shovel to make the pit waterproof and dig a shallow drainage ditch around and away from the pit to a lower level.

Small pits containing only a few bushels of vegetables or fruits will get sufficient ventilation if the bedding material over the vegetables extends through the soil at the top of the pile.

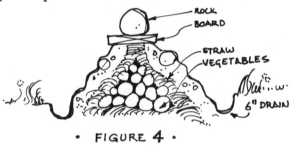

· FIGURE 4 ·

Cover the top of the pile with a board or piece of sheet metal to protect the stored produce from rain; a stone will hold the cover in place. To ventilate large pits, place two or three boards or stakes up through the centre of the pile of vegetables or fruits to form a flue. Cap the flue with two pieces of board nailed together at right angles. It's troublesome removing produce in the wintertime from these pits, and once opened, everything in the pit should be removed. A number of small pits are handier than a few larger ones. If you put a variety of vegetables in a number of small pits, it's a simple task to dig up one a week; but if you do it this way, separate the different types of vegetables with a layer of straw and *don't* put fruits and vegetables in the same pit.

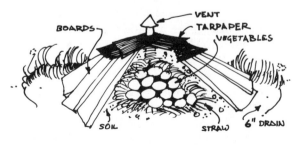

· FIGURE 5 ·

Here's another version of mound storage (fig. 5). A ventilating pipe can be included (to help stop decay), but must be capped in freezing weather. Drainage must be trenched around the mound.

Apples and cool vegetables (ones that require a storage temperatures close to 32°)may be stored in barrels sunk in the ground (fig. 5), preferably after packing in the early morning when it's cool. A pit is dug either in a well-drained level place or on a slope. It is lined with gravel or cinders for drainage and, after being put in place, lined with more gravel. The head of the barrel is covered with a burlap sack full of leaves and weighted down with boards and stones.

An open pit with hardware cloth screening and wooden lid works in a well-drained location. Store the root crops in sand until the pit is full. Cover with baled hay and a plastic cover.

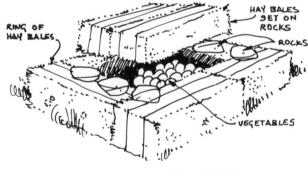

· FIGURE 6 ·

Hay bale storage can be done on top of the ground, which will be suitable for most crops. Make a rectangle of hay bales, with the centre partially hay-filled, and final bales for a lid. A stone can be placed under the top bales for ventilation, then removed when freezing weather prevails.

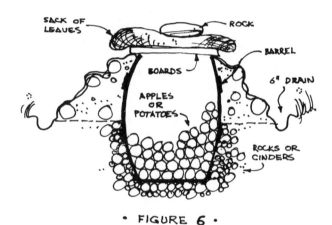

· FIGURE 7 ·

Large (18" x 30", or 24" x 24") tiles can be placed in a pit on well drained soil. Positioning should be near the kitchen and shaded from sun. As many as three to four baskets, boxes or other containers can be held in each pit. A simpler version of the tile pit consists of a 20-gallon garbage pail inserted into a hole. Produce can be placed directly into the pail, but there is some danger of rusting after several years of usage.

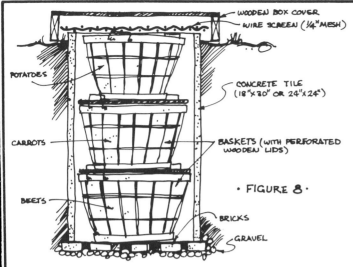

Figure labels: WOODEN BOX COVER, WIRE SCREEN (¼"MESH), POTATOES, CARROTS, BEETS, CONCRETE TILE (18"x30" OR 24"x24"), BASKETS (WITH PERFORATED WOODEN LIDS), BRICKS, GRAVEL

· FIGURE 8 ·

A box pit is another version which permits removal of small units at a time. Fruits or vegetables are stored in small boxes or baskets (one to two weeks' supply to a box). Remove them as you need them.

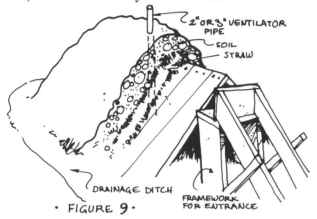

Figure labels: 2" OR 3" VENTILATOR PIPE, SOIL, STRAW, DRAINAGE DITCH, FRAMEWORK FOR ENTRANCE

· FIGURE 9 ·

Permanent Outside Storage

When you want something big, and permanent, you may as well build an outside storage shelter — in a bank, between two closely adjacent rises of ground, beside the foundation of an already erected building, or as a separate cellar.

If you have a farm which has a barn on it, here's a design which you might want to use or adapt for your own personal situation. This cellar was built next to the barn wall, beneath the barn approach (fig. 10). A section of the approach measuring 12 feet by 54 feet was removed and the earth wall was straightened in preparation for placing the forms to hold concrete.

Rough used lumber was utilized to build the forms, and cut lengths of 6-inch saplings (small logs) were used as supporting timbers. The earth wall on the north side and the stone wall of the barn (south side) eliminated several forms. After the concrete set overnight the forms were removed and used to support the roof slab. Thus the amount of form material was cut down. The walls and footings were poured of a lean mixture (cement one part; bank-run gravel, six). The roof slab was made of a one to three mixture. Some used brick and stones were thrown in with the concrete. A thin layer of heated road tar was brushed on the finished roof slab as waterproofing. This was reinforced with construction steel, since truck loads of five tons or more were passing over the barn approach. Plans of reinforcement can be obtained from construction steel manufacturers or their outlets.

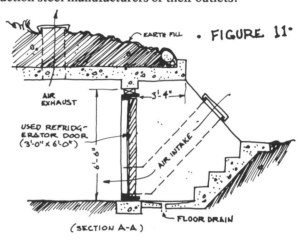

Figure labels: EARTH FILL, AIR EXHAUST, USED REFRIDGERATOR DOOR (3'-0" x 6'-0"), 3'-4", 6'-6", AIR INTAKE, FLOOR DRAIN, (SECTION A-A), · FIGURE 11 ·

One door opening was placed in each end of the storage-cellar, one square foot of door area for each 117 cubic feet of storage volume. Commercial cold storage doors were installed. You can probably find a set of these quite easily by keeping a lookout for a small butcher shop being demolished or selling out. Seven inlet and three outlet ducts were installed as ventilators. "Seconds" of 18 inch vitrified sewer tile were used for this purpose. Their location and number should be used to suit your individual conditions. The number used in this storage may have been excessive, though they will insure adequate ventilation under any condition and will prevent dead air pockets forming in the corners and elsewhere.

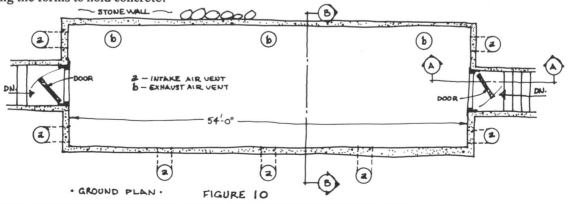

Figure labels: STONE WALL, DOOR, DN., a — INTAKE AIR VENT, b — EXHAUST AIR VENT, 54'-0", · GROUND PLAN ·, FIGURE 10

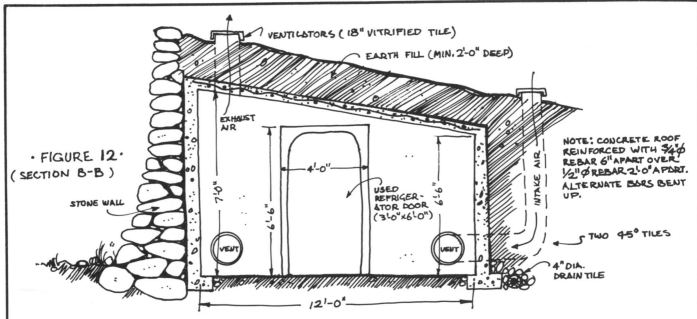

· FIGURE 12 ·
(SECTION B-B)

VENTILATORS (18" VITRIFIED TILE)

EARTH FILL (MIN. 2'-0" DEEP)

EXHAUST AIR

STONE WALL

7'-0"

6'-6"

4'-0"

USED REFRIGER-ATOR DOOR (3'-0"x6'-0")

6'-9"

INTAKE AIR

VENT

VENT

12'-0"

NOTE: CONCRETE ROOF REINFORCED WITH ¾"∅ REBAR 6" APART OVER ½"∅ REBAR 2'-0" APART. ALTERNATE BARS BENT UP.

TWO 45° TILES

4" DIA. DRAIN TILE

The air-intake area equals one square foot for each 340 cubic feet of storage capacity; the out-takes, one to 794 cubic feet. A 1/20 horsepower, airplane-propeller-type exhaust fan with 105-watt electrical in-put was installed to aid ventilation, but it isn't a necessity, merely an aid. The earth maintains a relative humidity satisfactory for the cool vegetable or fruit. If dry conditions are prevalent and you wish to maintain a high humidity, sprinkle water on the floor occasionally. A line of four-inch tile was laid just below the ground level inside the cellar at its periphery, connected with drain openings at each door and covered with cinders. The completed storage cellar has a minimum of two feet of earth fill, covered with sod on the roof and ends. This will prevent the entrance of frost through the roof slab, and the sod will help to maintain proper temperatures.

The tile vents at the surface of the ground have strong wooden and metal covers which cannot be injured by either animal or machine. Coarse mesh screens in all openings prevent rodents and trash from entering while the storage is being ventilated at night. Home made padded plugs fit into the tile openings from the inside and prevent air leakage during sub-zero weather.

If you are bothered by a high water table at certain times of the year, fig. 13 is a design for making watertight joints inside your storage cellar.

A Basement Storage Room

The storage room is a place where temperature and humidity are held to the proper level for keeping fruits and produce. This means lower than usual household or basement temperatures, ranging from 30° to 40° F. After deciding on the size and location (where low temperatures can be most easily maintained), the area must be insulated from temperatures prevailing in the rest of the house.

At least one wall having outside exposure should be used. A wall on the north side with a window that is easily reached is preferable. The other walls can be made of wood.

The walls to close off a corner of the basement are easily constructed with a two by four-inch framework, sheathing on both sides, and three-inch insulation batts between the studding. Leave an opening in one wall for a door. This may be framed with two by two-inch studs, faced on each side with quarter-inch plywood, and the centre filled with insulation. Fit the door tightly and secure it with a type of latch that holds it firmly closed. To insulate the ceiling of the storage space, sheath underneath the ceiling joists and apply three inches or more of insulation between the joists, extending the insulation out over the walls of the storage space.

It's advisable, when constructing the walls, to lay the floor plate on bricks (on edge) so that the finished walls are four inches off the floor. A form board on the

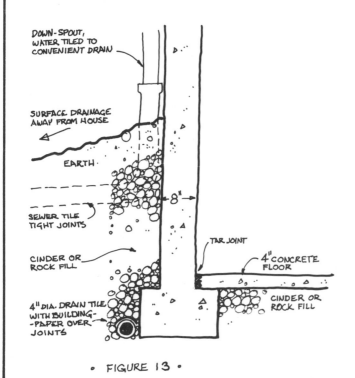

DOWN-SPOUT, WATER TILED TO CONVENIENT DRAIN

SURFACE DRAINAGE AWAY FROM HOUSE

EARTH

SEWER TILE TIGHT JOINTS

CINDER OR ROCK FILL

4" DIA. DRAIN TILE WITH BUILDING-PAPER OVER JOINTS

8"

TAR JOINT

4" CONCRETE FLOOR

CINDER OR ROCK FILL

· FIGURE 13 ·

outside will retain a straight line. With this arrangement, the wooden wall is away from water that is poured on the storage floor for the purpose of increasing the humidity.

Two types of insulating material can be used: *board* or *loose fill*. It is important to keep them dry or their insulating properties will be reduced. Moisture vapour barriers are used, inside and out, such as damp-proof paper, tar, or asphalt.

Board insulation (i.e., cork board) can be nailed to the walls and ceiling. Two thicknesses should be used to prevent leakage through joints.

Loose fill insulation includes planer shavings, cork dust, and minerals. The sheathing and damp-proofing should be done at the same time as you fill the wall space with insulation. Planer shavings work well for insulating the walls and ceiling, as they are dry and do not tend to settle. Add hydrated lime to the shavings (20 to 40 pounds per cubic yard) to help keep them dry. It also acts as a repellant to vermin and rodents. Tamp the shaves as they are filled between studs, until a density of seven to nine pounds per cubic foot is obtained.

For floor insulation, where it's required, use board-type insulation. The insulating board is laid and then mopped with hot tar. Cement or other flooring is laid on top. Where chinks occur at rough wall or floor surfaces, caulking compound is used to fill the space and protect the exposed insulating material from dampness.

The temperature of the surrounding basement will determine the thickness of the walls. A prevailing temperature of 60° F. outside the storage room calls for the following thickness of insulating materials:

Three inches: wood-fibre insulating board, cork board, granular cork, fibrous rock, rock wool.
Four to five inches: planer shavings
Six inches: compressed peat.

Lower basement temperatures will require less insulation.

The simplest method to provide ventilation is to open and close the storage room door, but preferably two windows should be available for intake and outlet ventilators. The ventilators may be of wood or, when possible, of tile, built into the foundation wall. The intake opening should be near or through the floor.

If you have a cellar with a window, here's the best arrangement. Remove the window entirely. Divide the

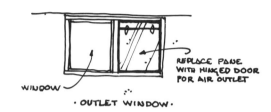

· OUTLET WINDOW ·

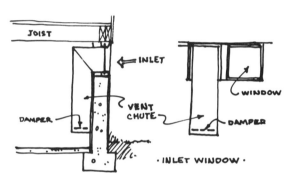

· FIGURE 15 ·

window frame either horizontally or vertically into two openings of equal size. Equip one opening with either a hinged or sliding door. Equip the other opening with an air duct that extends down to about one foot from floor level. Put a sliding door in this duct. If the window frame is divided horizontally, attach the cool air duct to the lower opening. Cover the outside of both openings with copper screening. When the doors are opened, cool air will come in via the air duct and warm storage air will go out the other opening. This arrangement provides better distribution and more effective cooling in the storage than merely opening a window. Take note: openings and ducts should be not less than one square foot in cross-sectional area. Light must be excluded from stored vegetables and fruits, so cover any excess window(s) with boards. If it gets extremely cold outside, you may have to open the door to let in a little warm air from the basement.

It's never advisable to have anything of wood permanently fixed to the floor; the dampness will rot it, and the extra surfaces and corners will form lodging places for molds, plant disease germs, and dirt. Portable slat floors in sections may be used to support barrels, boxes,

· FIGURE 14 ·

and crates. All shelves and bins should also be of slatted construction, to permit good air circulation. The bottom shelf or bin should be at least four inches above floor level, so that the floor can be cleaned underneath the shelf and water can be poured on the floor to maintain a high humidity.

Keep You Storage Area Clean

Give it a couple of coats of latex paint after it's finished. Wash it thoroughly after each storage season.

Stairwell Storage Room

If your house has a sloping cellar door and stairwell into the basement, this area can be adapted easily and cheaply.

· FIGURE 16 ·

The Sod and Log Root House

If you're high on energy and natural materials (logs and sod) and low on finances, here's an alternative to the standard type of construction.

Pick a spot (preferably a hillside or knoll, but a flat spot will work as well) and remove soil over a space a little bit larger than the ground plan of the root house and to the depth of two feet or more, providing there is no danger that the bottom will be wet. In the construction of the house, select poles or logs of two sizes, the larger ones being shortest; these are for the inside pen, as it is subjected to greater strain.

The ends of the logs are cut flat, so that they will fit down closely together, and make a pen that is nearly tight. At least two logs in each layer of the inner pen should be cut long enough to pass through and fit into the outer pen. These serve to fasten the two walls together. The space between the two is two feet on each side. Figure 14 shows the excavation and the beginning of the root house walls, with the method of "locking" them together. The doorway is built up by having short logs, which pass from one layer of poles to the other, and serve as supports to the ends of the wall poles.

The space between the two walls is filled with earth. Sods are used to fill in between the logs to block the earth. It's best to begin putting in the earth before the walls are completed, otherwise it will require an undue amount of hard lifting. When the walls are built up five to six feet on one side, and about two feet higher on the other (to give the necessary slope), the roof is put on. This is a good time to install a ventilation pipe. The roof should be of poles placed close together. Secure the poles to the logs and cover them with sod, 18 inches of earth, and sod again on the top. Two doors should be provided, one on the inner, and the other on the outer wall, both to fit closely. A filling of straw can be placed between the doors, if it is found necessary to do so to keep out the frost.

Bibliography

How to Grow Fruits by the Organic Method
Rodale
Rodale Books, Inc.

Encyclopedia of Organic Gardening
Rodale
Rodale Books, Inc.

Organic Gardening and Farming Magazine
Rodale
Rodale Books, Inc.

Five Acres and Independence
M.G. Kains
Greenburg, New York

Wood Heat Quarterly, Vols. 1 and 2
Lowther Press
Wolcoff, Vermont

Storing Vegetables and Fruits
U.S. Government Printing Office
Washington, D.C.

Home Storage of Vegetables,
Ontario Dept. of Agriculture
Parliament Buildings
Toronto, Ontario

A special thanks is extended to Rodale Publications for permission to use information from their books in this article.

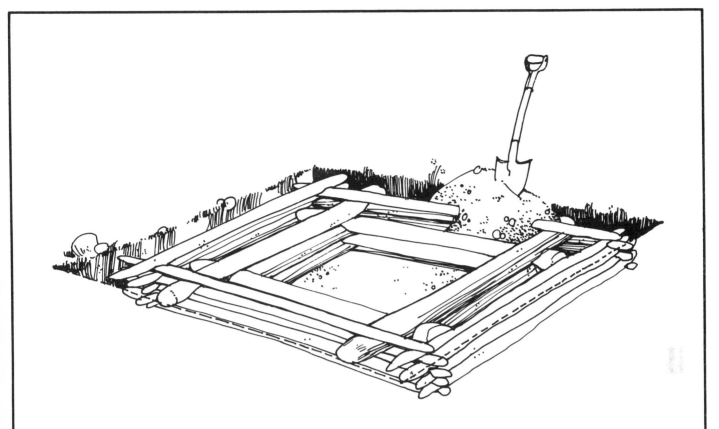

• DOUBLE WALLING OF SOD AND LOG ROOT HOUSE •

FIGURE 17
• THE SOD AND LOG ROOT HOUSE •

Poultry Housing

by Bus Hayden

Space

The most important principle in the housing of birds is that of space; available space determines the number and variety of fowl which can be kept. The recommended floor and roost space for the three main groups are as follows:

Breeds	Floor Space (per bird)	Roost Space (per bird)
Asiatics	4 sq. ft.	10 in.
Utility (American and English)	3 sq. ft.	8 in.
Mediterranean	2 to 3 sq. ft.	6 to 8 in.

Less than these amounts of space creates havoc: it promotes disease, cannibalism, and leaves the weaker birds no place to feed or roost adequately, making them unhappy "boarders."

Climate

The next most important item is climate. The climate of a chicken coop should, above all, be dry and free from draft. It requires adequate ventilation, but this can be obtained by having only one side of the house open, since a draft can only be created where there is both inlet and outlet for air currents. This open side should be facing away from the prevailing and storm winds: in our case, a western exposure is best. Where a western exposure isn't possible, either a roof vent, or vents around the windows (covered with cheesecloth or burlap) should suffice. When part of an existing building is being devoted to poultry, a draft-free roosting area can be achieved by placing the roosts in an adequate-sized box, which would consist of a floor or drop-board, three walls, and ceiling: the size of the box is determined by the number of roosts needed.

Temperature

Birds can withstand several degrees of frost, but temperatures over 75° F. can cause problems. Fowl which are confined at higher temperatures or with no shade become irritable and begin to peck at one another, especially during the moulting seasons (of which the chicks have three). The erupting of new pin feathers leads the birds to picking: when blood is drawn, it easily leads to cannibalism.

Lighting

Poultry must have adequate light in order to see and feed, for it identifies its food entirely by sight. A dull, gloomy coop leads to lethargic, non-active, non-producing birds. Birds do best in a well-lighted and well-ventilated coop, where there is an abundance of natural light which does not raise the temperature of the coop. In addition, it is highly recommended that all coops be whitewashed inside. This will reflect light, so that most of the floor space can be used for activity. Windows can afford to be fairly high where they receive direct light from the cooler winter sun, but not from hot summer sun. For maximum winter productivity, artificial light supplementing the natural daylight to maintain a 12-(or at most 13-) hour day is preferable. Light in excess of 13 hours can produce a false moult, and hence a cessation of egg production: less than 12 hours reduces egg production, for it takes roughly a 12-hour day to produce an egg. Birds, like all animals, are regular in their habits, and extensive variation in the hours of light will have a detrimental effect on production. Unless one can maintain a very regular artificial light supplement, it is preferable to depend on natural light, though production will be somewhat less.

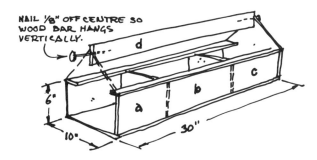

Feed Hopper—floor or stand

(a) grit box
(b) mash section
(c) oyster shell
(d) floating bar (1" x 4" with nails driven in ends; allows it to rotate)

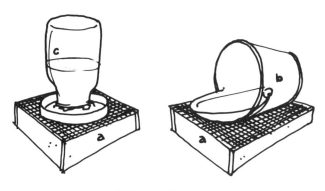

Water Stand

(a) box 2' square: tomato flat or frame covered with 1/2" mesh wire
(b) side pail
(c) glass fountain

Roosting

The bars on which the birds roost (approximately two-inch by two-inch stock is usual) are placed on the horizontal, above and parallel to a platform called a drop board. The first one is placed 8 to 10 inches out from the back wall, and subsequent ones at 16 to 20-inch intervals. The drop board should extend a further 16 inches in front of the front roost: this allows the birds to alight before seeking a spot on the roost. Drop boards should be a maximum of 30 inches from the floor of the coop. The roosts themselves should be six to eight inches above the drop boards for convenience in cleaning the latter. Fowl deposit over half their droppings at night; the use of the drop board thus helps to maintain a cleaner litter on the floor (bedding). It also makes available straight poultry droppings (manure), which when allowed to dry can be stored in empty feed sacks as an excellent fertilizer for plants requiring high nitrogen content. As for myself, I recommend the area under the drop board be used to house the community nest. As this space is visually dark, and therefore less effective for feeding activity, it makes an ideal nest site. I made a box using one-inch by eight-inch stock, three boards deep. This places the drop board at approximately 24 inches from the floor.

Exercise Yards

These are located by preference on the east or west side of the building, unless the southern exposure is fairly dense in plantings. Poultry enjoy morning and evening light; in the heat of the day, they are inactive and seek shade.

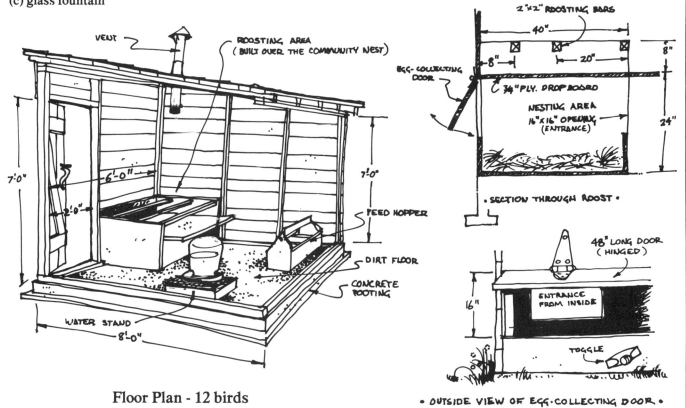

Floor Plan - 12 birds

Sauna

by Steve Terkel

We built our sauna out of a natural need for cleanliness; a means to cleanse one's body as well as a place of mental relaxation and enjoyment. It seemed simple enough: nothing more than fire, air, water, and stone. The notion of the sauna as a communal affair — a group endeavor, something to be enjoyed with others — was added incentive. The healthful and remedial effects were more apparent as we better understood the design, construction, and maintenance of the sauna.

First was the task of choosing a good sauna site. Since we had a river crossing our land, it was a matter of selecting a spot deep enough for the "plunge," a ritual very much a part of the sauna. The plunge and the accompanying rush of cooling sensations is a stimulating exchange for the intense heat of the sauna bath.

The traditional sauna is a one-room structure, with a wood-burning stove as the heat source. The interior is constructed in a series of platform levels to allow the bathers to move higher as they desire hotter temperatures. The best material for sauna construction is seasoned rough wood, as it enables moisture to be absorbed and the necessary amount of air to pass through the walls. Our sauna was built using recycled barn lumber. It took lots of nail pulling, but by using recyclable materials we kept the cost way down and might have saved some trees too. Besides, green lumber is likely to warp, come apart at the seams, or develop cracks and openings. If new lumber is needed, make sure that only kiln-dried lumber is used for the interior of the sauna.

The sauna is designed to breathe; that is, allow some circulation of air. In order to insure a proper heat chamber, take care to seal any cracks in the upper part of the sauna. Since heat rises, a well-insulated, tight roof will retain heat the longest. Any leaks in the floor or lower walls should also be sealed, but don't worry if you can't get them all. Traditional sauna walls are built

loosely at the bottom to provide the necessary ventilation. The door should be low, as should any windows. Use a rather small door, so that too much heat does not escape when it is being opened and closed. We lined the interior walls with cedar shakes; it's a very porous wood and has a pleasant fragrance. Don't paint or oil the walls, as this will restrict the normal circulation of the air.

The sauna has withstood 2,000 years of almost consistent design and few will dispute that the wood-fueled sauna is still the best. Our sauna is heated by a medium-sized wood stove, with stones piled on top. Sauna heat is non-radiant; that is, the heat is absorbed by the stones, then circulated throughout. This is dry, indirect, penetrating heat. Choose the stones carefully; they should neither expand nor crumble. A good size is slightly bigger than a grapefruit. Dark-coloured river rock is a start; if in doubt, bang it with a hammer; if it breaks, keep looking.

The firing up of the sauna is a sort of ritual in itself. Much care is taken to fire it well in advance, to insure that it is completely heated before the bathers enter. Some maintain that the "ripening" of the sauna is like the tuning of an orchestra before a concert. Usually we burn a hard-wood like oak with some fir and heat it for two to three hours. It seems that the longer the sauna is heated the better and more efficiently it will function.

The sauna bath is essentially immersion in hot dry air; the temperature ranges from 170° to 220° F. The whole purpose is to perspire thoroughly, thereby cleaning the pores, toning the body, and inducing relaxation. The body perspires more in dry heat than in moist heat. The drier the air, the more heat the bather can stand. Some real sauna freaks take saunas as hot as 250° F. The heat is the difference between the sauna and the steam bath or the sweat lodge. It is easier to stand tempera-

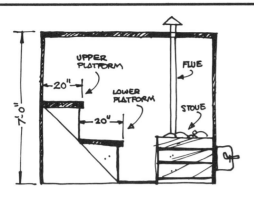

Side View

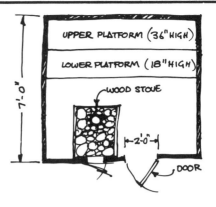

Top View

tures of 190° to 212° F. in dry air than one of 120° F. in water-saturated air. When water is sprinkled on the hot rocks in the sauna, the increased humidity is even dry, as the steam is quickly absorbed by the walls. This dry steam quickens perspiration from already open pores and cleanses more effectively.

Here are some thoughts on the "how to" aspects of taking a sauna:

(1) Take a 10 to 15 minute sauna at 180° to 200° F. A lower heat may be preferred by beginners.

(2) Sprinkle water on the rocks to increase humidity 10 per cent. Use water sparingly, so that steam is distributed evenly.

(3) Beating oneself with birch leaves loosens dirt and stimulates the cells. The whisk is usually birch, but oak works fine. It is a bundle of small leafy branches tied at one end, then soaked in hot water to soften it before use.

(4) Whisking is usually followed by washing and a quick dip in a lake or stream to cool off.

(5) Return to the sauna, take a position on highest and hottest platform, and repeat the procedure. This period of perspiration and whisking may be shorter than the initial one. A third time may be desired.

(6) Finish with a final plunge in a lake or stream, or in winter a roll in the snow. Movement should be calm and deliberate. It's quite a rush: the sharp contrast is pleasantly invigorating, and not the shock that some imagine.

(7) Let yourself dry naturally in fresh air, as cooling off is very important. Don't dress until body temperature has returned to normal.

(8) A 10 to 15 minute rest should always follow. The sauna is a very calming peaceful experience: don't rush it, you've got all the time in the world.

A really good sauna book (perhaps the only one) is:
Sauna, The Finnish Bath
by H.J. Viherjuuri
Stephen Green Press
Brattleboro, Vermont.

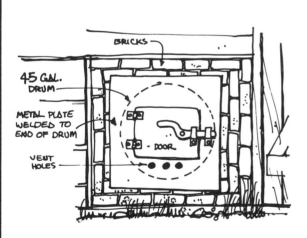

Front View of Stove

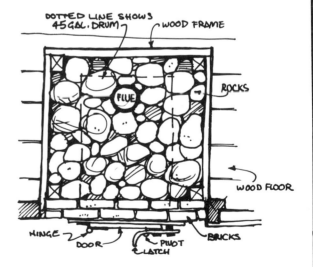

Top View of Stove

The stove should be totally enclosed by rocks. This is best done by building a wood frame around the stove, netting the frame in with wire mesh and then piling the enclosed area with rocks.

If possible, build the stove into a wall so that the door faces outside. This will allow you to fire the stove without having to enter the sauna.

A stove can easily be made out of an old forty-five gallon oil drum; weld a door on one end and attach a stove pipe.

Harnessing the Small Stream

by C.D. Basset

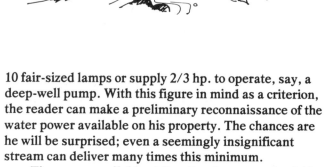

Many farms, ranches, and other fair-sized tracts of land embrace at least one brook within their limits. In most cases, the idea that a small stream can provide a useful source of power has never occurred to the property owner or, if it did, has been rejected as silly. The fact remains, nevertheless, that impressive advantages can spring from small water-power installations.

Electricity can be generated for general use, for pumping water, and for stand-by or emergency purposes; and the pond that is usually created can serve additionally as a means for watering livestock in dry times, for fire-fighting, as a swimming pool, as a place to raise fish for sport or as a "crop."

Power can be obtained from any flowing stream, no matter how small. Whether it is desirable to harness this power depends on two factors. First, does water flow all the year round, even in the late summer months? Second, does enough water flow to make the harnessing of it economically sound? The first factor is, of course, known to the property owner by observation; the second may be determined by simple measurements.

What's the least amount of power that is worth developing? There is in this country at least one water-wheel manufacturer who makes a line of small-capacity units, and this company's smallest hydroelectric unit develops 1/2 kilowatt. From this it can be inferred that, in this company's experience, it is not economically wise to harness a stream that will not develop at least 500 watts dependably at the switchboard. Half a kilowatt will light

10 fair-sized lamps or supply 2/3 hp. to operate, say, a deep-well pump. With this figure in mind as a criterion, the reader can make a preliminary reconnaissance of the water power available on his property. The chances are he will be surprised; even a seemingly insignificant stream can deliver many times this minimum.

The power available at the site of a water wheel (that is, before deductions for inefficiencies in the wheel and generator) is expressed in this formula:

$$\text{H.P.} = \frac{62.4 \times Q \times H}{33,000}$$

Here Q is the cubic feet of water passing through the wheel in one minute; H is the "head" or vertical distance in feet through which the water falls; 62.4 is the weight in pounds of one cubic foot of water; and 33,000 the number of foot-pounds per minute in 1 horsepower. A number of methods exist by which the variables Q and H can be determined, but before considering them, it's well to examine first the possible sites for the dam and wheel, since they will necessarily affect the amount of head secured.

The location of the dam, as suggested in Figure 1, should be governed by two principles. It should be placed where the greatest useful head is obtainable; that is, where the greatest fall occurs in the shortest length of stream. Such a site is often indicated by a natural waterfall, by a conspicuously steep slope, or by the swiftness of the current. The second locating principle is a simple matter of cost: a dam should be placed where it can be smallest and still impound the most water. This means, in general, that it should be placed where the stream valley or cut is narrowest.

The site of the water wheel (Fig. 2) may be either at the dam or some distance below it. The former location is the more common, being simpler to build and eliminating the need for a pipe or penstock to deliver water to the wheel. Disadvantages include the fact that the spillway must be of ample capacity to protect the powerhouse in time of high water, and the fact that only the "artificial head"—that created by the dam itself—is available. In cases where the ground falls away abruptly below the dam site, the "divided-flow" layout may be desirable, for it greatly increases the head.

Another preliminary calculation should be made as to the height of the proposed dam. This is restricted, as a rule, only by the height of the valley walls at the site, and by the materials, equipment, and money available for building it. The higher it is, the greater the head and the larger the pond that will be created. "Pondage"—water stored for use in times of peak demand — is an important factor in water power calculations. Power is rarely needed 24 hours a day, and construction of a dam of sufficient height to provide water storage will greatly increase the power available at the time of day required.

If, for example, a wheel is to be run for 16 hours a day, and if a dam is built that will impound all water

FIGURE 1 LOCATING THE DAM

IF LOCATED AT A WATER-FALL, RIGHT, A DAM WILL OFTEN BE SMALL AND INEXPENSIVE AND THE TOTAL HEAD FAIRLY LARGE.

A WIDE VALLEY CALLS FOR A LONG DAM, AS HIGH AS POSSIBLE TO PROVIDE THE MAXIMUM HEAD.

SWAMPY MEADOWLAND INDICATES THE PRESENCE OF A NATURAL RESERVOIR. PLACE THE DAM AT THE NARROWEST POINT WHERE THE BROOK LEAVES.

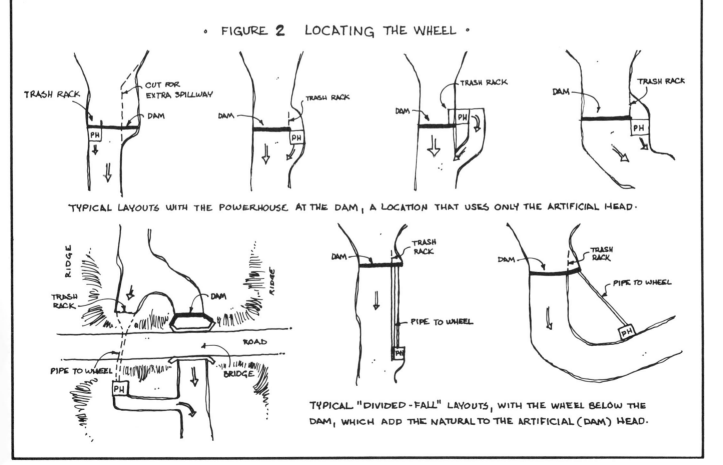

FIGURE 2 LOCATING THE WHEEL

TYPICAL LAYOUTS WITH THE POWERHOUSE AT THE DAM, A LOCATION THAT USES ONLY THE ARTIFICIAL HEAD.

TYPICAL "DIVIDED-FALL" LAYOUTS, WITH THE WHEEL BELOW THE DAM, WHICH ADD THE NATURAL TO THE ARTIFICIAL (DAM) HEAD.

flowing into the pond during the idle eight hours, the power capacity will be increased by 50 per cent. Don't neglect to distinguish between "live storage"—the volume of water represented by the difference in height of the spillway flash boards and the wheel intake — and "dead storage"—the volume of water below the level of the wheel intake. The former is power banked against a time of need; the latter is worthless, powerwise.

Once the dam and powerhouse are tentatively sited, and the height of the first is provisionally set, it is time to measure the power available. Assume that all water flowing in the stream can be made to flow through the wheel, which is a fair assumption on small installations. This flow (Q in the power formula) can be determined by the "weir method," which involves constructing a temporary dam of controlled proportions, or by the "float-method," which is theoretically a trifle less accurate, though still quite satisfactory.

The float method (Fig 3) involves the formula:

$$Q \text{ equals } A \times V \times 60$$

in which Q is the volume of water flowing in cubic feet per minute, A is the cross-sectional area of the stream in square feet at the site, and V is the average velocity of the stream at this point, expressed in feet per second.

Select a length of the stream that is fairly straight, with sides approximately parallel, and unobstructed by rocks or shoals for a distance of about 100'. Stretch a taut wire squarely across the stream near the middle of this length and measure the width of the stream here in inches. Mark this width off on the wire and divide it into 10 equal divisions. From the centre point of each division, measure the depth of the water in inches. Then average the depth figure by adding each value and dividing by 10. The cross-sectional area of the stream, A, is now sec-

ured by multiplying this average depth by the width, and dividing the result by 144 to obtain the answer in square feet.

Your next step in determining Q is to measure the rate of flow. Using a steel tape, mark off a course along the bank that is 100' long: the mid-point of this course should be at the line where the cross-section was measured. Stretch wires or rope tautly across the stream at each end of the course, and make a float by filling a bottle so that it rides awash. Provide it with a pennant so that you can follow it easily. Then set the float adrift in the middle of the stream, timing its progress over the course with a stop watch, beginning just when the pennant passes the first wire and stopping just as it passes the second.

Make a series of runs, averaging the results. The speed of the float in feet per second is then the length of the course divided by the average time. This result is not, however, suitable for immediate use in the flow formula, since not all the water in a stream flows as rapidly as that in the centre and near the top. If you multiply the float speed by the coefficient 0.83, the resultant value will serve as V in the flow formula.

Given an estimate of the amount of head to be present at the wheel, you can now make a rough determination of the horsepower your stream can provide. It's worth emphasizing, though, that this figure is necessarily only as accurate as the measurements that produced it, and that the power indicated is that present *at the time of measuring.* A single stream-flow value is not of itself particularly useful unless it is obtained at the time of lowest water, usually in the late summer months. Moreover, even if you have measured the flow at slack-water time, the figures should if possible be supplemented by others secured during maximum springtime flow, so that you can calculate the size of spillway needed to prevent damage to your installation in times of high wa-

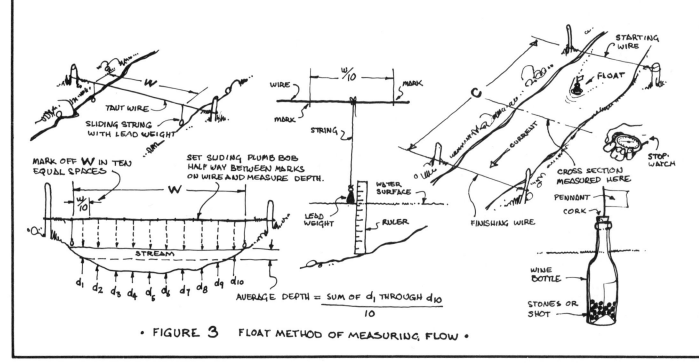

· FIGURE 3   FLOAT METHOD OF MEASURING FLOW ·

ter.

It's a good practice, for backyard engineers as well as for professionals, to refine, cross-check, and test your measurements by all means at your disposal. Such checks will not only reduce the chance of disappointment in the final result, but will also permit calculated economics in construction and greater efficiency in operation.

Before you begin even a preliminary reconnaissance of waterpower on your property, the writer suggests you secure a looseleaf notebook to be devoted solely to the project. Develop the habit of neatly entering all data as it is obtained, not forgetting to note dates and stream conditions at the time measurements are made. Such a record is a great help in performing sound calculations and producing excellent results.

Putting Water to Work

Measuring the flow of water in the stream or brook on your property is the logical first step in planning a small waterpower project. The float method of making this measurement is generally the easiest to perform and, if done carefully, is accurate enough for most purposes. If, however, a stream is so shallow at low-water time as to impede the progress of a weighted float, the weir method of measuring flow has advantages. Essentially a kind of water meter, a weir is a rectangular notch or spillway of carefully controlled proportions located in the centre of a small temporary dam. Two simple measurements permit the volume of flow to be accurately calculated.

Before constructing the dam, measure the depth of the stream at the site; the depth of the weir notch (M in Fig. 4) should equal this. Since the dam need not be permanent, a simple plank or tongue-and-groove lumber will serve adequately. No water must flow except through the weir, so care should be taken to seal the ends and bottom of the dam by extending planks into the banks and below the bed of the stream. Clay or loam puddling on the upstream side will stop minor seepage. Be sure the dam is perpendicular to the flow of the stream.

The weir should be located in the centre of the dam, with its lower edge not less than 1' above the surface of the water below the dam. This lower edge should be accurately leveled. Both this and the vertical edges of the weir should be beveled with the sharp edge upstream; a 1/8" flat on the bevel will keep the edge from breaking down. Proportion the weir so that its length L is not less than 3M, and larger if possible.

Drive a stake in the stream bed at least 5' upstream from the weir, pounding it down until its top is exactly level with the bottom edge of the weir. Allow the stream to reach its maximum flow through the weir and then measure with a ruler the depth in inches of water over the stake. Referring to the table on this page, you can now read the number of cubic feet per minute of water for each inch of L, the weir width. If you multiply the figure from the table by L, the result is the total amount of water flowing in cubic feet per minute, which is Q in the horsepower formula.

If your stream is already dammed, there is no need to construct another dam just to measure flow. It is quite possible to employ the existing dam, using its spillway as a weir, provided that all water can be made to pass through the spillway. Construct a wooden or metal frame to fit the spillway and seal it in place snugly. The centre of this frame should incorporate a properly proportioned weir notch. As before, M should equal the depth of the water flowing through the spillway before the weir is installed, and L may in most cases be half the width of the spillway.

To get an accurate estimate of available horsepower, you will need a precise figure for H, the head of water that will be present. *Head* may be defined as the vertical distance in feet from the surface of water in the pond behind the dam to the surface of the stream below the dam at the site of the wheel. This figure may be obtained by any of several methods in cases where a dam is already present, and with scarcely greater difficulty at the site of an unbuilt dam.

Measuring a difference in elevation can be quickly and accurately done with an engineer's transit and leveling rod. But since not everyone has access to these instruments, and since thos who do would not need instructions on so simple a joo as running a level, we'll pass on to other methods.

Figure 5 illustrates a very simple way of measuring a vertical distance. The equipment required is a carpenter's level, a folding rule or steel tape, a 1" by 2" by 6' board with two edges planed parallel, two wooden pegs, a stake, and a C-clamp. These are items that can be found in almost any home, and certainly any farm.

Depth D Inches over stake	1/8"	1/4"	3/8"	1/2"	5/8"	3/4"	7/8"
1 inch	.40	.47	.55	.65	.74	.83	.93	1.03
2 "	1.14	1.24	1.36	1.47	1.59	1.71	1.83	1.96
3 "	2.09	2.23	2.36	2.50	2.63	2.78	2.92	3.07
4 "	3.22	3.37	3.52	3.68	3.83	3.99	4.16	4.32
5 "	4.50	4.67	4.84	5.01	5.18	5.36	5.54	5.72
6 "	5.90	6.09	6.28	6.47	6.65	6.85	7.05	7.25
7 "	7.44	7.64	7.84	8.05	8.25	8.45	8.66	8.86
8 "	9.10	9.31	9.52	9.74	9.96	10.18	10.40	10.62
9 "	10.86	11.08	11.31	11.54	11.77	12.00	12.23	12.47
10 "	12.71	12.95	13.19	13.43	13.67	13.93	14.16	14.42
11 "	14.67	14.92	15.18	15.43	15.67	15.96	16.20	16.46
12 "	16.73	16.99	17.26	17.52	17.78	18.05	18.32	18.58
13 "	18.87	19.14	19.42	19.69	19.97	20.24	20.52	20.80
14 "	21.09	21.37	21.65	21.94	22.22	22.51	22.70	23.08
15 "	23.38	23.67	23.97	24.26	24.56	24.86	25.16	25.46
16 "	25.76	26.06	26.36	26.66	26.97	27.27	27.58	27.89
17 "	28.20	28.51	28.82	29.14	29.45	29.76	30.08	30.39
18 "	30.70	31.02	31.34	31.66	31.98	32.31	32.63	32.96
19 "	33.29	33.61	33.94	34.27	34.60	34.94	35.27	35.60
20 "	35.94	36.27	36.60	36.94	37.28	37.62	37.96	38.31
21 "	38.65	39.00	39.34	39.69	40.04	40.39	40.73	41.09
22 "	41.43	41.78	42.13	42.49	42.84	43.20	43.56	43.92
23 "	44.28	44.64	45.00	45.38	45.71	46.08	46.43	46.81
24 "	47.18	47.55	47.91	48.28	48.65	49.02	49.39	49.76

Table from James Leffel & Co.

This table shows the quantity of water passing over a rectangular weir in cubic feet per minute (cfm) for each inch of notch width. Depth D is read as a combination of the left-hand column and the top row. For example, if the depth over your stake is 5⅜", follow over 5 (fifth row) to ⅜ (fourth column), and read the value as 5.01 cfm. Don't forget that this figure should now be multiplied by the width in inches of your notch.

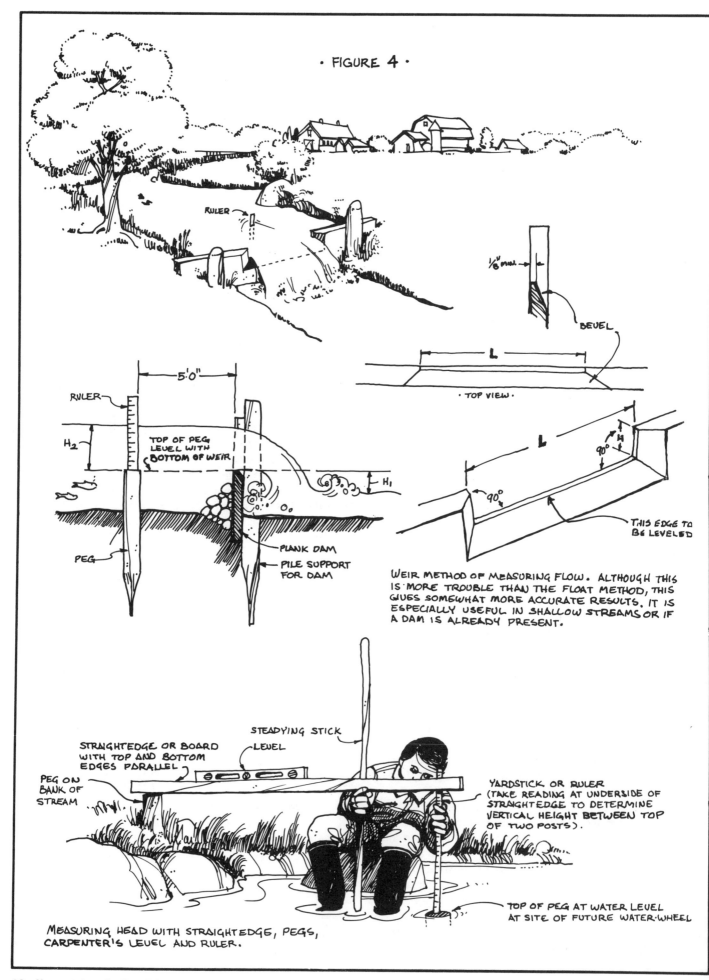

· FIGURE 4 ·

RULER

1/8" min.

BEVEL

· TOP VIEW ·

L

5'0"

RULER

H₂

TOP OF PEG LEVEL WITH BOTTOM OF WEIR

H₁

PEG

PLANK DAM

PILE SUPPORT FOR DAM

L

90°

90°

H

THIS EDGE TO BE LEVELED

WEIR METHOD OF MEASURING FLOW. ALTHOUGH THIS IS MORE TROUBLE THAN THE FLOAT METHOD, THIS GIVES SOMEWHAT MORE ACCURATE RESULTS. IT IS ESPECIALLY USEFUL IN SHALLOW STREAMS OR IF A DAM IS ALREADY PRESENT.

STEADYING STICK

STRAIGHTEDGE OR BOARD WITH TOP AND BOTTOM EDGES PARALLEL

LEVEL

PEG ON BANK OF STREAM

YARDSTICK OR RULER (TAKE READING AT UNDERSIDE OF STRAIGHTEDGE TO DETERMINE VERTICAL HEIGHT BETWEEN TOP OF TWO POSTS).

TOP OF PEG AT WATER LEVEL AT SITE OF FUTURE WATER-WHEEL

MEASURING HEAD WITH STRAIGHTEDGE, PEGS, CARPENTER'S LEVEL AND RULER.

Though the method can be somewhat tedious if the difference in elevation is large, the results will be quite accurate with ordinary care in leveling and measuring. Note in the drawing that in the case of a pre-existent dam, one or more measurements needed to carry around the edge of the dam are subtracted from, rather than added to the total.

Less practical in most cases, though still of occasional special value, are two other ways to determine head. Elevations can be measured quite readily by the techniques of photographic surveying. For those who are familiar with the procedure, it is a simple matter to take the required pictures in the field and then scale the required elevation at the desk from the developed photographs. Another method involves the use of a barometer, either mercury or aneroid, to indicate differences in height. However, this method is useful only where the head to be measured is considerable, say, more than 25', and calls for special techniques to hold the probable error down to acceptable proportions. Except in unusual circumstances, the writer recommends that the method in Figure 5 be employed, inasmuch as it requires little special equipment and with ordinary care gives good results.

With sound figures for both H and Q, you are now ready to calculate the available horsepower of your installation with the formula given previously. If the power is found to be sufficient to warrant continuing with the project, say 2/3 hp. at the least, your next step is to determine the nature of your power requirements. Here individual variations are so many as to make it difficult to outline a specific procedure. It's possible, however, to suggest factors you should consider in planning your power plant.

Some of the uses to which small-capacity installations are successfully put include directly powering pumps, mills, machine tools, or other small-demand machinery; and driving a generator to supply electricity for either lighting or power purposes. The latter type of installation is of course the more flexible and generally useful. Determine, then, the uses you propose for your water power, and tabulate the horsepower required after each item. In the case of electric motors or appliances rated in amperes or watts, remember that watts are volts times amperes, and that 746 watts are equal to one horsepower.

From this tabulation, the peak load can be determined. This is the sum of the power demands made by different pieces of equipment that may probably be in use at one time. Knowing power and load, you can now determine if the proposed installation will be on a sound basis.

Do not use your available horsepower figure directly, since deductions should first be made for losses in the water wheel and in the generator, if you intend to be using one. For small installations, assume wheel efficiency to be 75 per cent; many small wheels will better this, but the assumption will provide leeway for possible optimism in measuring H and Q. Generator efficiency can be assumed to be 80 per cent, a figure that will also be bettered in many cases, but is on the safe side. Thus switch-

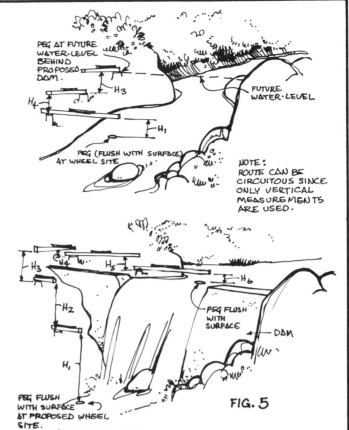

NOTE:
ROUTE CAN BE CIRCUITOUS SINCE ONLY VERTICAL MEASUREMENTS ARE USED.

FIG. 5

MEASURING HEAD. WITH A CARPENTER'S LEVEL, STRAIGHTEDGE, AND PEGS, HEAD CAN BE MEASURED BEFORE OR AFTER DAM IS BUILT.

board power may be expressed at .75 x .8 x hp, or .6 of the available horsepower.

At this stage of the game, it's well to mull over the possible variations and combinations, rather than to proceed with specific construction plans. Consider for example the decision required if the indicated switchboard power will seemingly handle the peak load — whether to build a dam just large enough to do this job, or to build one substantially larger to handle possible future increases in power requirements. The former choice will be obviously cheaper at first, but may not be so in the long run, since power demands have a way of growing and since it is rarely satisfactory to increase the structure of an existing dam.

If the peak load is apparently too high, various possibilities should be considered. Will "pondage"—water stored behind the dam overnight or in slack periods — help out? Can the use of equipment be dispensed with? Is the project necessarily a year-round enterprise, or can the low-power characteristics of the dry season be ignored? A word of caution on these points may not be amiss: it's far better to plan an installation that will provide more power than you need than one which doesn't supply enough.

Whether, in the event that you decide to generate electricity, to use AC or DC is another decision to make. In circumstances where the generator must be located some distance from the load, AC is the only choice, for DC transmission losses would be too high, amounting in small installations to a prohibitive percentage of switch-

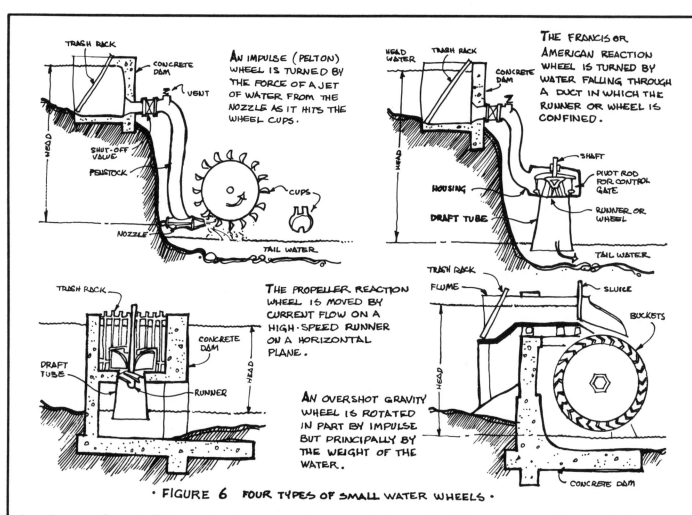

TRASH RACK

CONCRETE DAM

VENT

AN IMPULSE (PELTON) WHEEL IS TURNED BY THE FORCE OF A JET OF WATER FROM THE NOZZLE AS IT HITS THE WHEEL CUPS.

HEAD

SHUT-OFF VALVE

PENSTOCK

CUPS

NOZZLE

TAIL WATER

HEAD WATER

TRASH RACK

CONCRETE DAM

THE FRANCIS OR AMERICAN REACTION WHEEL IS TURNED BY WATER FALLING THROUGH A DUCT IN WHICH THE RUNNER OR WHEEL IS CONFINED.

HEAD

HOUSING

DRAFT TUBE

SHAFT

PIVOT ROD FOR CONTROL GATE

RUNNER OR WHEEL

TAIL WATER

TRASH RACK

CONCRETE DAM

DRAFT TUBE

HEAD

RUNNER

THE PROPELLER REACTION WHEEL IS MOVED BY CURRENT FLOW ON A HIGH-SPEED RUNNER ON A HORIZONTAL PLANE.

FLUME

TRASH RACK

SLUICE

BUCKETS

HEAD

AN OVERSHOT GRAVITY WHEEL IS ROTATED IN PART BY IMPULSE BUT PRINCIPALLY BY THE WEIGHT OF THE WATER.

CONCRETE DAM

· FIGURE 6 FOUR TYPES OF SMALL WATER WHEELS ·

board power. If your buildings and equipment are already wired to receive one type of current, it would obviously be sensible to fix on the same type of power; if for example your farm is already wired for a battery-type lighting system, there would be little reason to revamp the installation for AC. If, on the other hand, you are starting from scratch, I recommend the use of DC wherever possible. An AC generator must be closely regulated at or slightly above synchronous speed, and close regulation requires complicated governing equipment that is tricky to build or expensive to buy. A compound-wound DC generator, on the other hand, provides inherently close voltage regulation over a wide speed range; and even a shunt-wound DC generator with a direct-acting field-rheostat regulator would be satisfactory.

Selecting the right wheel for your plant is perhaps the final step in your preliminary planning. There are three general types of water wheel — impulse, reaction, and gravity — and several fairly common varieties of each type. However, for small plant purposes, it is possible to narrow the number down to those shown in Figure 6. Note that two types of reaction wheels, the Francis and the propeller, are shown, and but one variety of gravity wheel, the overshot one.

The impulse or Pelton wheel, operated exclusively by the force of the water from the jet, includes among its advantages very slight leakage and friction losses, good efficiency under varying flows, and a sufficiently high

shaft speed to drive a generator. It is more resistant to pitting by water containing sand, silt, or minerals than the reaction type. Its disadvantages include the fact that it cannot use all the available head, is larger than a reaction wheel developing the same power, and will wallow in high tail water. It must be mounted as close to the tail water as possible.

The reaction wheel, either the Francis or propeller type, is turned by the fall of water through a duct or pipe in which the wheel is confined. It is the most compact of all wheels for a given power, uses all of the available head, and operates at a satisfactory speed for direct coupling to a generator. It is an efficient wheel over a wide range of conditions, and it can be mounted at any convenient height above tail water. Disadvantages include rapid corrosion with silted water, and relatively high leakage and friction losses, especially in small units.

Finally, there is the overshot gravity wheel, which is turned largely by the weight of the water and partly by impulse. It has good efficiency under varying flow, and is unaffected by sand, silt, or minerals in the water. Gravity wheels turn at a low speed, which is undesirable for driving a generator or high-speed machinery, but suitable for some pumping and grinding applications. Such a wheel will wallow in high tail water, is the largest wheel for given power, and will be obstructed by ice in winter unless housed.

Dams Turn Water Into Kilowatts

Concrete, though desirable, isn't necessary for damming a small stream. Beavers have gotten by for years without it. Suitable materials can be found on almost any farm. Logs, rough-hewn timber, rock, masonry, planking, gravel, sand, and clay are all useful. Choose the materials most readily available on your property, or the least expensive if you must obtain them elsewhere.

You will have determined the height and width of the dam you will need to convert your stream to power. The summer months provide an ideal time for its construction, for then most brooks are at their lowest level and the water will not impede the progress of work.

Four basic types of small dams are shown in the accompanying drawings. All are adaptable in general to the kind of materials likely to be on hand and also to the head of power desired.

There are two basic principles of design to bear in mind no matter which you build. First, a dam should be sealed both above and below its foundation to prevent the seepage of water through or under it. Seepage through a dam, if permitted, weakens the structure and will eventually break it; that under a dam will undermine its foundation. Then, too, some means must be provided to prevent undermining of the dam by the water that flows or spills over it.

In addition, you should check with your local authorities and possibly file plans for your dam with them. General supervision comes under the Water Board.

Figure 7 illustrates the earth dam. Sealing this type of dam is most important, since seepage will literally carry it away if allowed to progress. The seal is put in first and the dam built around it. How far down it should go depends upon the kind of soil. A sand foundation, for instance, requires the seal to extend deeper than clay. If planking is used, it would be well to apply a protective coat such as tar or creosote.

A general pattern for depositing the earth fill is shown in the drawing, but it is not necessary to follow it unless different types of earth are available. Deposit the fill by layers, rolling and tamping each layer well. Then protect the waterside surface from erosion by covering it with a matting woven from brush. Plant turf on the top and downstream side to hold the earth.

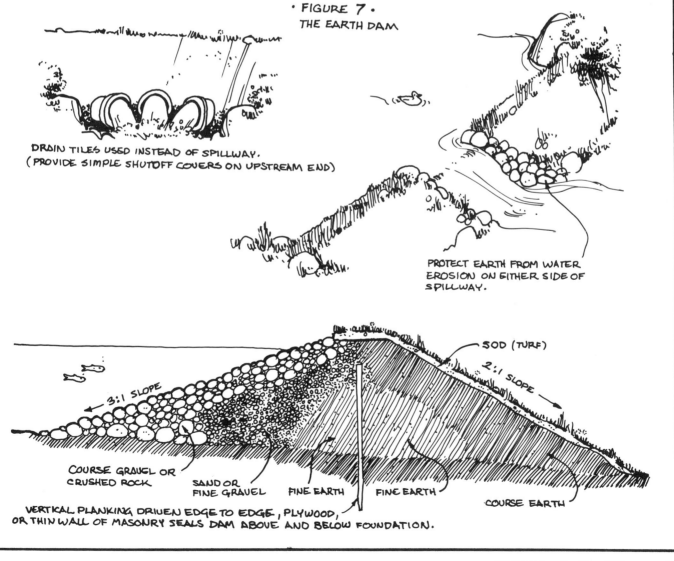

· FIGURE 7 ·
THE EARTH DAM

DRAIN TILES USED INSTEAD OF SPILLWAY.
(PROVIDE SIMPLE SHUTOFF COVERS ON UPSTREAM END)

PROTECT EARTH FROM WATER EROSION ON EITHER SIDE OF SPILLWAY.

SOD (TURF)
2:1 SLOPE
3:1 SLOPE
COURSE GRAVEL OR CRUSHED ROCK
SAND OR FINE GRAVEL
FINE EARTH
FINE EARTH
COURSE EARTH
VERTICAL PLANKING DRIVEN EDGE TO EDGE, PLYWOOD, OR THIN WALL OF MASONRY SEALS DAM ABOVE AND BELOW FOUNDATION.

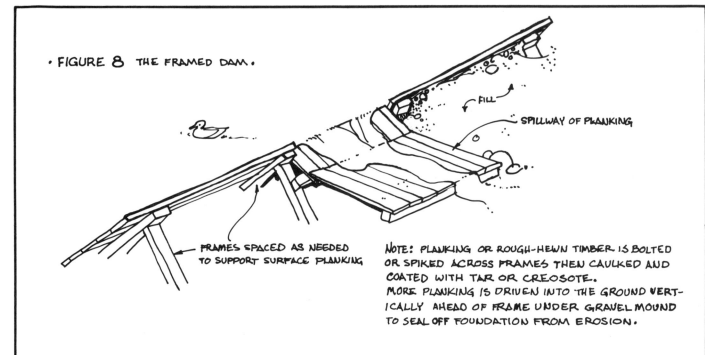

• FIGURE 8   THE FRAMED DAM.

— FILL

— SPILLWAY OF PLANKING

← FRAMES SPACED AS NEEDED TO SUPPORT SURFACE PLANKING

NOTE: PLANKING OR ROUGH-HEWN TIMBER IS BOLTED OR SPIKED ACROSS FRAMES THEN CAULKED AND COATED WITH TAR OR CREOSOTE.
MORE PLANKING IS DRIVEN INTO THE GROUND VERTICALLY AHEAD OF FRAME UNDER GRAVEL MOUND TO SEAL OFF FOUNDATION FROM EROSION.

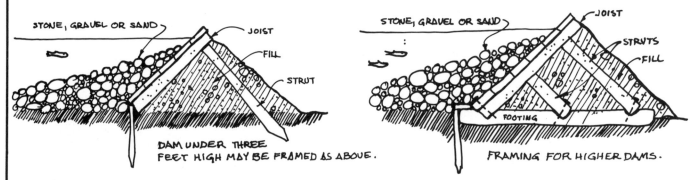

STONE, GRAVEL OR SAND

JOIST
FILL
STRUT

DAM UNDER THREE FEET HIGH MAY BE FRAMED AS ABOVE.

STONE, GRAVEL OR SAND

JOIST
STRUTS
FILL
FOOTING

FRAMING FOR HIGHER DAMS.

Such a dam obviously cannot have water spilling over its crest, since this action would wash it away. Two suggestions for handling the excess water are shown. The spillway must be of some material, such as masonry or planking, resistant to the erosion of rushing water, and the sides must protect the open ends of the earth dam from spillage water. An alternative method of handling runoff water is with drain tiles instead of a spillway. Some means must be provided for shutting them off. A simple cover on the upstream end would serve.

Figure 8 shows the framed dam, which likewise can be easily built, particularly on a farm where lumber in any form from logs to planks is abundantly available. Each frame consists of one joist, on which the surface timber is laid, and one or more struts. Once the height of the dam is determined, the size of individual frames will vary depending on the contour of the gulley, those frames located at the lowest part being the largest. The frames are spaced according to the support the surface timber needs; that is, the thinner the surfacing, the more supports needed.

Lay the planking surface or rough-hewn timber horizontally and edge to edge across the frames, and bolt or spike each in place. Caulk the joints and apply a protective coating. Fill is put in behind the downstream side. Build the spillway entirely of planking or similar materi-

al.

The gravity dam (Fig. 9) relies upon its weight for its stability. This dam would be most feasible where large rocks or field stones abound. Bricks, concrete or cinder blocks, and even chunks of broken concrete pavement are also excellent materials. The dam is strictly a masonry type, each block being laid with mortar.

Length is not a critical factor for any of these three dams, but it is important for the arch dam (Fig. 10). The placement of such a dam in a gulley is limited not only to the point of least width, but also to the point where the banks are highest. Otherwise, this dam would impound little water. It would seem unwise to build one to span a width of more than 10'. If the heavy timber is used only as a frame on which to spike or bolt a surface of planking, as shown in one of the drawings in Figure 10, the number of timber arches will depend on the strength of the planking and also on the height of the dam.

Only early foundations are considered in the drawings, but you may be fortunate enough to have a solid rock foundation on which to build. In that case a seal below the foundation will not be necessary, but some means must be provided to anchor the dam to the rock, such as with anchor bolts in the case of either the framed or gravity dam. Likewise the dam should be sealed at the rock foundation to prevent seepage under it.

• FIGURE 9 •
THE GRAVITY DAM

ROCK, GRAVEL OR SAND.

BRICK, CONCRETE BLOCK, CINDER BLOCK, BROCKEN PAVEMENT, OR FIELDSTONE

In most instances it will be found best to restrict the width of the spillway for excess water to some part of the total length of the dam. This will always be necessary in the case of an earth dam, to prevent washing. The spillage water may be allowed to pour over the entire length of framed, gravity, and arch dams, however, if the precautions shown in Figure 11 are taken.

If the downstream side of the dam, or of the spillway, is a curved hard surface of masonry or timber approximating the natural curvature of the water flowing over, it will guide the spillage water so it will be directed downstream without actually falling. Such a curved spillway surface is particularly satisfactory for an earth dam. Large rocks, bricks, or other hard objects placed on the downstream side of a spillway not having a curved surface will break the force of the free-falling water and prevent erosion.

The spillway in its simplest form takes the shape of a rectangular depression in the crest of the dam. It should usually be large enough to carry off sufficient excess water, so that impounded waters will not top the dam at any season of the year. This, of course, is quite a problem, since accurate determination of spillway capacity requires a knowledge of the total area drained by the creek being dammed, plus data on the amount of rainfall at all seasons.

However, most of us will know whether or not the creek we are damming stays within its banks during the year. If it does, then a safe rule to apply would be to make the area of the spillway equal to the cross-section area of the creek at the dam when it is brimful or just ready to flood. The formula is illustrated in Figure 11.

If the stream does flood, then either construct a dam that in an emergency can allow water to top its full length or build some sort of floodgate into the dam so it can be opened when necessary. One form such a floodgate could take is a group of drain tiles through the dam, as shown in Figure 7.

The height of the dam you build will be determined by the area of the land to be covered by the impounded water. In general, the higher the dam, the greater the area covered by water above it.

All vegetation, brush, floatage, and the like in the area to be flooded, and for about 15' around it, should be burned out or otherwise cleared before the dam is built. This keeps down the breeding of mosquitoes and helps retard pollution. It is required in the regulations of some states and is a wise precaution even when not covered by law. In addition, all trees in the area to be flooded should be cut reasonably close to the ground.

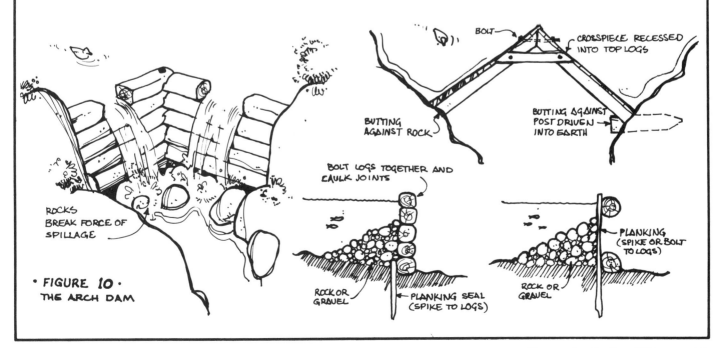

• FIGURE 10 •
THE ARCH DAM

ROCKS BREAK FORCE OF SPILLAGE

BUTTING AGAINST ROCK

BOLT LOGS TOGETHER AND CAULK JOINTS

ROCK OR GRAVEL

← PLANKING SEAL (SPIKE TO LOGS)

BOLT

CROSSPIECE RECESSED INTO TOP LOGS

BUTTING AGAINST POST DRIVEN INTO EARTH

PLANKING (SPIKE OR BOLT TO LOGS)

ROCK OR GRAVEL

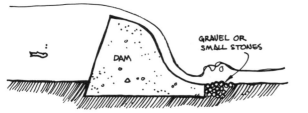

• CURVATURE OF SPILLAGE APPROXIMATED WITH MASONRY •

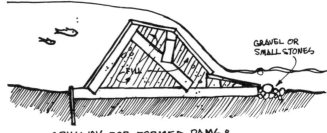

• SPILLWAY FOR FORMED DAMS •

• FIGURE 11 •
METHODS OF PREVENTING SPILLAGE FROM UNDERMINING DAM

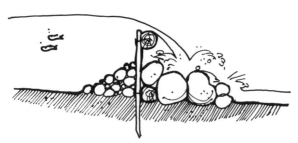

• ROCKS BREAK FORCE OF SPILLAGE •

$$L \times H = W \times D$$
L IS LENGTH OF SPILLWAY
H IS DEPTH OF SPILLWAY
W IS AVERAGE WIDTH OF BRIMFULL CREEK
D IS FULL DEPTH OF CREEK

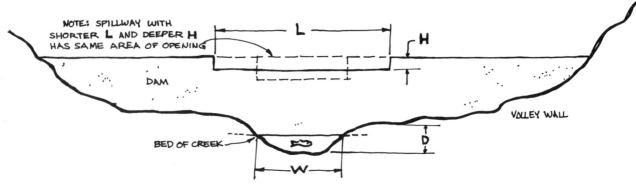

NOTE: SPILLWAY WITH SHORTER **L** AND DEEPER **H** HAS SAME AREA OF OPENING

Building An Overshot Wheel

Often seen beside a picturesque rural mill, an overshot water wheel possesses two excellent characteristics — considerable mechanical efficiency and easy maintenance. Many have remained in service for decades.

Operated by gravity, the overshot wheel derives its name from the manner in which water enters the buckets set around its periphery. Pouring from a flume above the wheel, the water shoots into buckets on the down-moving side, overbalancing the empty ones opposite and keeping the wheel in slow rotation.

Such a wheel may be located near, but not actually in a stream. If a site on dry ground is chosen, the foundation may be constructed dry and the water led to the wheel and a tailrace excavated.

It should be noted, however, that an overshot wheel is practical only for a small-capacity output. How much power it will produce depends upon the weight of water the buckets hold, and its radius or lever arm. Expressed in another way, the output depends upon the weight of water transported and the height, or head, through which it falls while in the buckets. For maximum efficiency, the wheel must use the weight of the water through as much of the head as possible. Therefore, the buckets should not spill or sling water until very near tail water.

Power Increases with Width

Although of simple construction, an overshot wheel is cumbersome in size. For this reason, before attempting to build one, be certain you have the facilities to move and lift it into place when completed. Also allow yourself plenty of working floor space. It must be under-

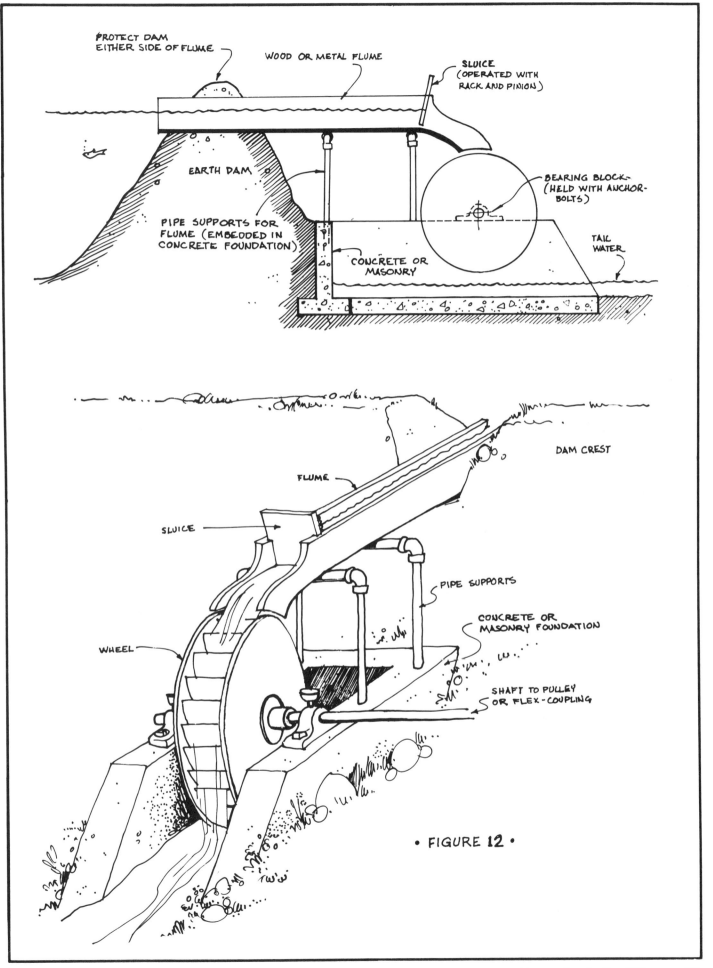

PROTECT DAM
EITHER SIDE OF FLUME

WOOD OR METAL FLUME

SLUICE
(OPERATED WITH
RACK AND PINION)

EARTH DAM

BEARING BLOCK
(HELD WITH ANCHOR-
BOLTS)

PIPE SUPPORTS FOR
FLUME (EMBEDDED IN
CONCRETE FOUNDATION)

CONCRETE OR
MASONRY

TAIL
WATER

DAM CREST

FLUME

SLUICE

PIPE SUPPORTS

CONCRETE OR
MASONRY FOUNDATION

WHEEL

SHAFT TO PULLEY
OR FLEX-COUPLING

· FIGURE 12 ·

Harnessing the Small Stream   53

stood, too, that such a wheel is a sizable project and requires a lot of material and time. Extreme care in cutting and assembling the parts is not essential, however, because the wheel, operating at slow speed, need not be accurately balanced.

Accompanying this article are drawings that illustrate the construction of a small wheel suitable for a water head of 6'3''. The wheel itself has a diameter of 5', leaving a flume head of 15'' to propel the water into the buckets. As shown in the table at the bottom of page 56, you may build the wheel to give a power output ranging from 1/2 hp. to 1 hp. at 10 r.p.m. All dimensions remain the same except the width, the horsepower increasing as this is increased. For 1/2 hp., the wheel should be 15-31/32'' wide. For 1 hp., it should be 31-29/31.'' Before deciding on the wheel size, read Guy Immega's article on page 57.

Virtually all large wheels are built with wood or steel arms, as in the drawing above, and have a shroud plate only around the outer edge, but you may find it simpler and more satisfactory to build the drum-type wheel described here. In this case, each shroud plate is a disc of 1/8'' sheet steel sole plate to which it is continuously welded by the buckets, by one of the two large diameter 1/4'' steel hub flanges to which it is also continuously welded, and by the long hub itself.

Large Sheet Required

If preferred, the shroud plates may be made of wood. If so, care should be taken to bolt them securely to the hub flanges. Bushings pressed into the wood for bolts will give the wheel a longer life expectancy.

Sheet steel for the discs may be ordered direct from several large companies, in case your local supply house is unable to furnish it. Ordinarily, such steel comes in standard 48'' widths, so you may have to weld together two or more sheets to get the required 5' diameter, using either a butt weld or a backing plate. This will produce some distortion or ripple, as will the welding on of the numerous clips required. So long as distortion is local, however, and the main lines of wheel and shaft remain true, this will do no harm.

After the sheet has been prepared, scribe a 5' circle on it and cut it with the cutting flame of a gas welding torch. With ordinary care, this method should give sufficient accuracy. Vent and drainage holes should be drilled as indicated around each disc to lessen corrosion with the drum.

Good Buckets Important

The buckets are the most important element of the wheel. To give maximum efficiency, they must be formed so that the water enters smoothly at the top of their travel and remains in them until just before they reach the bottom. For this reason, the bucket form indicated on page 55 should be followed faithfully. Either sheet metal or wood is an acceptable material, but metal is better suited to cold climates, since wood is damaged when ab-

sorbed water freezes. Because the buckets are subject to wear from the water and sediment that it carries along, you may want to install them so they can be easily replaced.

In laying out and making wooden buckets, follow these steps:

Using a common centre, strike off two arcs, one with a 21-1/2'' radius and the other with a 2'6'' radius. Then draw a radius line intersecting these arcs.

From the point where the radius crosses the outer arc, draw a chord 10-1/2'' long and, from the new point where this intersects the outer arc, draw a line to point E. You now have the inner trace of the bucket.

Take a piece of the bucket stock and lay it along the upper edge of this inner trace, and you have a cross-section through the bucket. Cut your stock accordingly, making the length equal to B in the table of dimensions.

Steel Buckets Require Jig

Steel buckets are only slightly more difficult, if you follow these steps:

Using a common centre, strike off two arcs on a piece of plywood, one with a 21-1/2'' radius and the other with a 2'6'' radius.

Draw a radius line and then a tangent to the inner arc, making it vertical to the radius. From the point of tangency, measure 5'' along the tangent. Mark this point.

Using this mark as a centre, strike off an arc with a 5'' radius. This is part of the inner trace of the bucket.

At the point where the original radius line (step 2) crosses the outer arc, draw a chord 10-1/2'' long, and at point F where this chord intersects the outer arc, draw a new radius line. Also at point F, measure off 15° of the new radius and draw line FG 11-1/2'' long.

Then, using G as a centre, strike an arc with an 11-1/2'' radius. This forms the rest of the inner trace of the bucket.

Cut the plywood along this line and along the lines that form a quarter ellipse. Using this as a pattern, cut several more quarter ellipses from scrap. Nail these to stretchers to make a bending jig around which the buckets may be formed.

Weld Wheel Parts

Welding of the various parts of the wheel produces an exceptionally strong construction. After getting together or making all the required parts, begin the assembly by welding four clips to each end of the hub sleeve. Then weld the required number of clips to the shroud plates for the sole plate, and weld the shroud plates to the clips on the hub sleeve. After welding both hub flanges to the shroud plates and the sleeve with a continuous weld, attach the sole plate to the clips on the shroud plates with No. 8 self-tapping screws. Also weld the sole plate to the shroud plates with a continuous weld, and the bucket-support angles to the sole plate.

Attach wooden buckets to the supports with 3/4'' No. 10 roundhead wood screws. If you use steel buckets, rivet or screw 10 clips to each side of each bucket and attach the buckets to the angles with No. 8 self-tapping screws. Then drill holes through the shroud plates in the way of the clips for the same type of screws.

Lubricate Bearings Well

Using locknuts and washers, fasten the hub sleeve to the shaft with two 3/8'' by 4-1/2'' bolts, placed at right angles to each other. Two bearing mountings having 2-3/8'' renewable liners with shoulders should be bolted to the foundation. Place shims about 1/4'' thick under the bearings.

Standard bearing mountings, variously called pedestals or blocks, may be bought complete with wick oiler or cup oil reservoir and with built-in self-aligning features. Standard bronze-bearing metal liners or inserts likewise may be bought from any machine component supplier. Babbitt liners are equally satisfactory.

Although the wheel turns slowly, it is heavy and will be running almost constantly, so good lubrication of the bearings is essential. To this end, care should be taken to insure that the bearing liners are finished to the correct fit. Porous inserts or inserts containing graphite are excellent for this application, but may cost more than regular bearing inserts.

It is important that the foundation be carried deep enough so that water falling from the buckets will not undermine it. Avoid a long flume if possible, in order to keep the construction as simple as possible. Strengthen it along its entire length with an exterior frame and support it well from dam to wheel with pipe uprights.

Sluice Governs Wheel

The sluice gate may be located at any convenient place along the flume. Since it is the governing mechanism of the wheel, its installation should be anything but slipshod. If it is installed at an angle, as on the following page, water pressure will keep it at any desired position. If installed vertically, some mechanism, such as a rack and pinion, should be provided to keep it in place.

Adjust the sluice so that the buckets will run one-quarter full. This will give a wheel speed of 10 r.p.m. If the buckets are allowed to run more than one-quarter full, the efficiency of the wheel will drop for two reasons. Because of the increased speed, centrifugal force will throw water from the buckets. They also will begin to spill before approaching tail water. Although this practice does waste water, it may be profitably employed during freshet to increase the power output, for at such times the excess water would be wasted anyway.

· FIGURE 13 ·

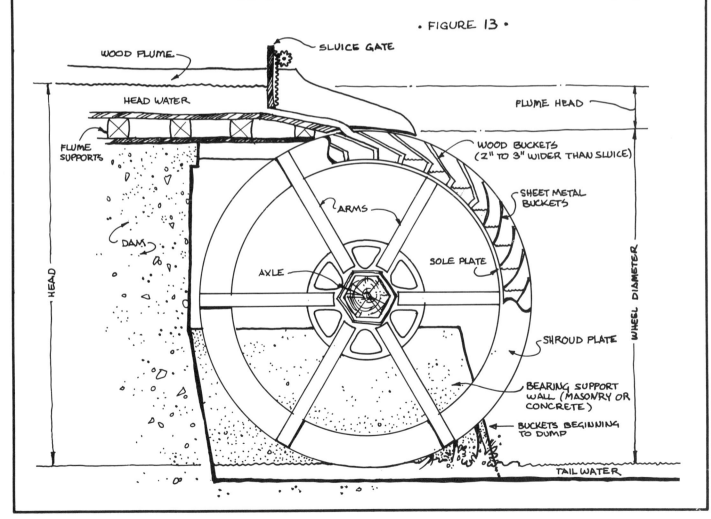

• FIGURE 14 •

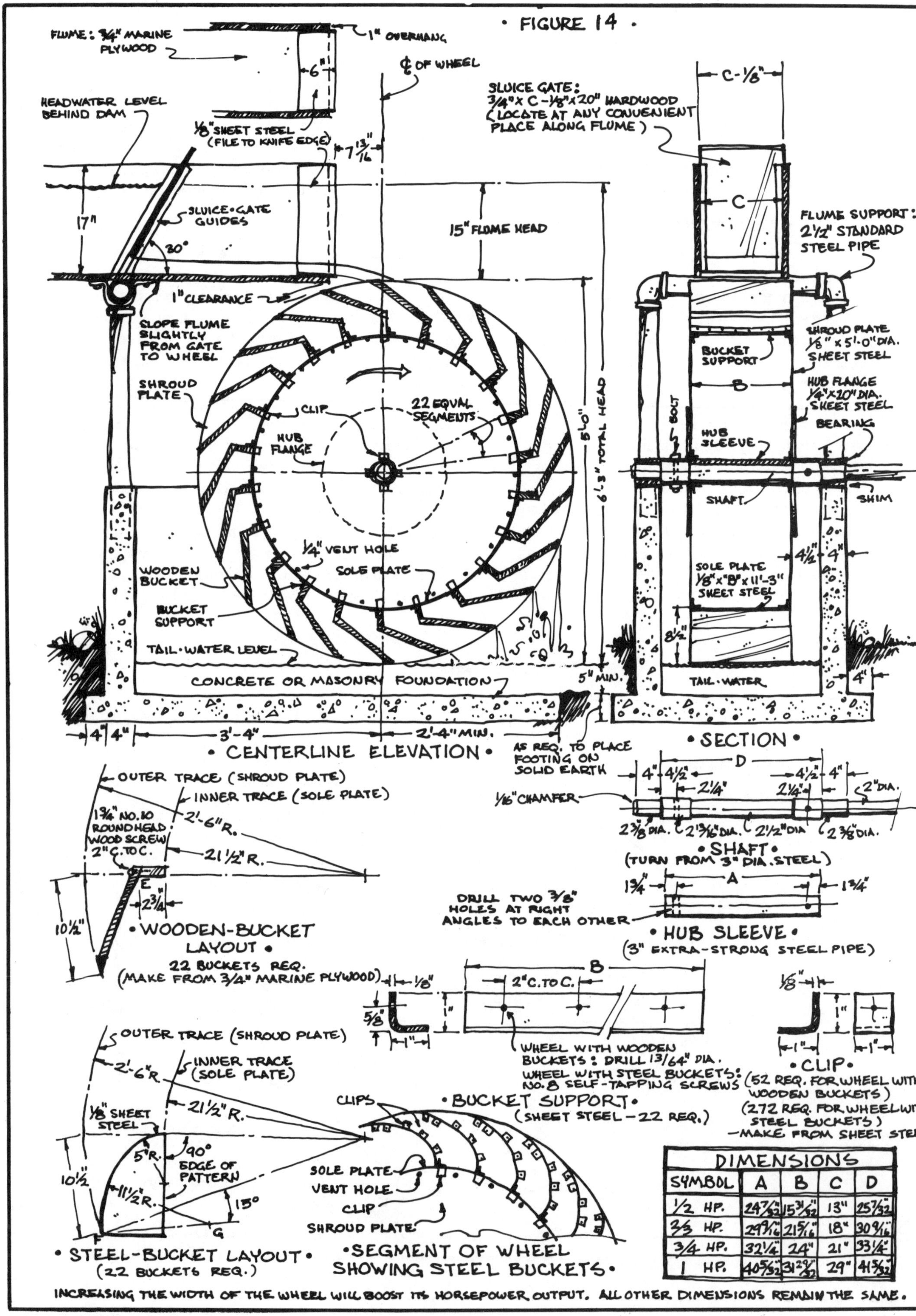

FLUME: 3/4" MARINE PLYWOOD
1" OVERHANG
6"
℄ OF WHEEL
HEADWATER LEVEL BEHIND DAM
1/8" SHEET STEEL (FILE TO KNIFE EDGE)
7 13/16"
17"
SLUICE-GATE GUIDES
30°
15" FLUME HEAD
1" CLEARANCE
SLOPE FLUME SLIGHTLY FROM GATE TO WHEEL
SHROUD PLATE
CLIP
22 EQUAL SEGMENTS
HUB FLANGE
5'-0"
6'-3" TOTAL HEAD
1/4" VENT HOLE
WOODEN BUCKET
SOLE PLATE
BUCKET SUPPORT
TAIL-WATER LEVEL
CONCRETE OR MASONRY FOUNDATION
5" MIN.
4" 4"
3'-4"
2'-4" MIN.
AS REQ. TO PLACE FOOTING ON SOLID EARTH
• CENTERLINE ELEVATION •
SLUICE GATE: 3/4" x C-1/8" x 20" HARDWOOD (LOCATE AT ANY CONVENIENT PLACE ALONG FLUME)
C-1/8"
C
FLUME SUPPORT: 2 1/2" STANDARD STEEL PIPE
SHROUD PLATE 1/8" x 5'-0" DIA. SHEET STEEL
BUCKET SUPPORT
B
HUB FLANGE 1/4" x 20" DIA. SHEET STEEL
BOLT
BEARING
HUB SLEEVE
SHAFT
SHIM
4 1/2"
4"
SOLE PLATE 1/8" x 8" x 11'-3" SHEET STEEL
8 1/2"
TAIL-WATER
4"
• SECTION •
D
4" 4 1/2" 4 1/2" 4"
2 1/4" 2 1/4"
2" DIA.
1/16" CHAMFER
2 3/8" DIA. 2 13/16" DIA. 2 1/2" DIA 2 3/8" DIA.
• SHAFT •
(TURN FROM 3" DIA. STEEL)
1 3/4" A 1 3/4"
DRILL TWO 3/8" HOLES AT RIGHT ANGLES TO EACH OTHER
• HUB SLEEVE •
(3" EXTRA-STRONG STEEL PIPE)
OUTER TRACE (SHROUD PLATE)
INNER TRACE (SOLE PLATE)
2'-6" R.
21 1/2" R.
1 3/4" NO. 10 ROUNDHEAD WOOD SCREW 2" C. TO C.
E
2 3/4"
10 1/2"
• WOODEN-BUCKET LAYOUT •
22 BUCKETS REQ.
(MAKE FROM 3/4" MARINE PLYWOOD)
1/8"
5/8"
1"
B
2" C. TO C.
1"
WHEEL WITH WOODEN BUCKETS: DRILL 13/64" DIA.
WHEEL WITH STEEL BUCKETS: NO. 8 SELF-TAPPING SCREWS
• BUCKET SUPPORT •
(SHEET STEEL — 22 REQ.)
1/8"
1"
• CLIP •
(52 REQ. FOR WHEEL WITH WOODEN BUCKETS)
(272 REQ. FOR WHEEL WITH STEEL BUCKETS)
— MAKE FROM SHEET STEEL —
OUTER TRACE (SHROUD PLATE)
INNER TRACE (SOLE PLATE)
2'-6" R.
21 1/2" R.
1/8" SHEET STEEL
5" R.
90° EDGE OF PATTERN
10 1/2
11 1/2" R.
15°
F
G
• STEEL-BUCKET LAYOUT •
(22 BUCKETS REQ.)
CLIPS
SOLE PLATE
VENT HOLE
CLIP
SHROUD PLATE
• SEGMENT OF WHEEL SHOWING STEEL BUCKETS •

DIMENSIONS

SYMBOL	A	B	C	D
1/2 HP.	24 7/32"	15 31/32"	13"	25 7/32"
2/3 HP.	29 9/16"	21 5/16"	18"	30 9/16"
3/4 HP.	32 1/4"	24"	21"	33 1/4"
1 HP.	40 5/32"	31 29/32"	29"	41 5/32"

INCREASING THE WIDTH OF THE WHEEL WILL BOOST ITS HORSEPOWER OUTPUT. ALL OTHER DIMENSIONS REMAIN THE SAME.

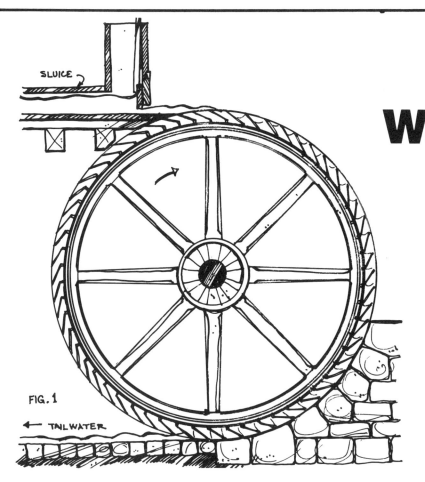

SLUICE

FIG. 1

← TAILWATER

Water Wheel Design

by Guy Immega

Choice of Wheel

There are three basic types of traditional water wheels. The overshot wheel takes water in at the top and discharges it at the bottom. The breast wheel takes water in somewhere in the middle of the wheel and discharges it at the bottom. The undershot wheel (Poncelet) both accepts and discharges water at the bottom.

The choice of wheel design depends largely upon its location. If you have a high head of water (20 feet or more), then an overshot wheel is a good choice, because a fairly narrow wheel (small volume) can be built and no complicated breastworks are required. A disadvantage of the overshot wheel is that it requires an elevated feed trough, and a power license (since the water is taken out of the stream bed).

A breast wheel is suitable for falls of between 5 and 15 feet. It is more difficult to build, because a breastwork (a shaped shoulder under the wheel designed to retain water on the wheel) is required, and the wheel must be wider to get the same power out.

A Poncelet undershot wheel is suitable for falls under seven feet. It must be very wide (for the same power), and requires a fitted race beneath the wheel.

For heads of 50 feet or more, a Pelton wheel is a good choice. Pelton wheels require very little water and a long feed pipe.

Overshot and High Breast Wheels

The simplest and most efficient of traditional water wheels are the overshot and highbreast wheels. Water enters at or near the top of the wheel, is carried down one side of the wheel in buckets, and is discharged at the bottom. The power of the wheel is not derived from the speed of the water entering the wheel, but from the force of gravity acting on the loaded side of the wheel — thus deriving the classification of "gravity wheels" (as opposed to impulse wheels and turbines). Gravity wheels in general are large in diameter, and operate at slow speed with high torque.

Overshot: An overshot wheel (fig. 1) is usually constructed with a nearly horizontal feed trough such that the water will enter the buckets with a velocity somewhat greater than the wheel, so as not to be struck by the back of the buckets and be thrown off the wheel. A sluice gate is generally provided at the end of the pentrough to regulate the amount of water in the feed trough. An important modification of the overshot wheel is the pitch-back wheel, in which the direction of waterflow is reversed in the pentrough so that water may smoothly enter the wheel, and exit so that the bottom is eight or nine inches above the tailrace (level of millpond); then the direction of the water will be reversed as the water falls out of the wheel into the tailrace, thus allowing a pitch-back wheel to rotate in the opposite direction, and use a straight pentrough feed.

A weakness in the design of overshot wheels is that water begins to be discharged at a point above the bottom of the wheel, and thus escapes before it has done all

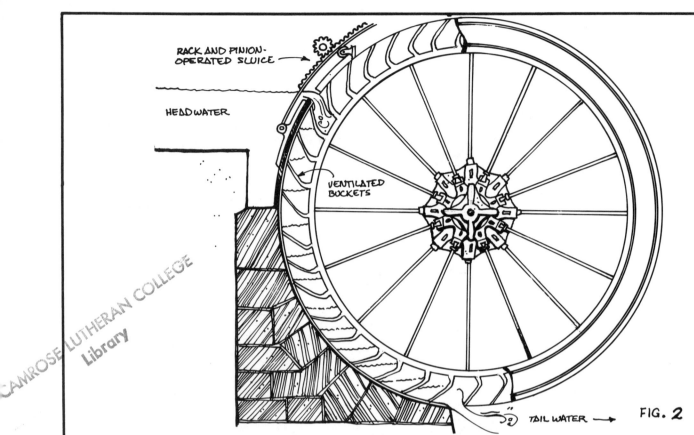

CAMROSE LUTHERAN COLLEGE
Library

RACK AND PINION-
OPERATED SLUICE

HEADWATER

VENTILATED
BUCKETS

TAIL WATER →

FIG. 2

the work due to the fall. Three solutions to this problem are: (1) use a curvilinear form of bucket; (2) only partly fill the buckets (build a wider wheel); (3) build a close fitting-stationary breast to retain the water on the lower half of the wheel. Overshot wheels are from 60 to 75 per cent efficient, and require 12 to 10.8 cubic feet per second, to obtain one horsepower per foot of fall.

Breast Wheels: Breast wheels generally receive water below the top of the wheel, and have a close-fitting breast to keep water on the wheel. Some designs include a curved feed sluice gate which is lifted to obtain closure — rather than lowered — so that water entering the wheel will be at maximum possible elevation; this scheme allows the water to enter the wheel at variable levels, according to the height of the river. The design of this sluice gate is more complicated, as it usually is curving to fit the wheel, and must fit tightly at the bottom so as not to leak water to a lower portion of the wheel. After the sluice gate, there are often guide plates to divide the water into the wheel.

The design of the buckets on breast wheels is different from overshot wheels. The difference is that the buckets are ventilated, so as to allow air to escape as they are being filled. This obviates the problem of incomplete filling. There are two basic types of ventilated buckets: with and without a sole plate. The sole plate is a hoop of material as wide as the wheel, which isolates the back of the buckets from the inside of the wheel. Ventilated buckets without a sole plate allow air and excess water to vent to the interior of the wheel. Ventilated buckets with a sole plate allow air and excess water to vent to the next highest bucket. Obviously, the ventilated bucket with sole plate is the most efficient.

In high breast wheels of 25 feet in diameter or larger, the breast is not required as the buckets have narrower openings (as with an overshot wheel), and to retain water longer on the wheel. In this case, the loss due to spilling does not warrant the effort involved in building a high and close-fitting breast. Breasts can be constructed from wood and sheet metal, or from masonry. To be most efficient, they should be close-fitting. With a close-fitting breast, care must be taken to avoid having large foreign objects enter the wheel, as they will get caught between the wheel and the breast and cause damage. Breast wheels should always be mounted above the tail water, and the bottom of the breast itself should stop about 10 inches from the extremity of the vertical diameter of the wheel. Both precautions are designed to prevent wheel drag. The efficiency of breast wheels is about 60 per cent.

Wheel speed: The speed of the periphery (edge) of overshot and breast water wheels is usually between four and six feet per second. A minimum velocity of three feet six inches per second is standard for falls of 40 to 45 feet,

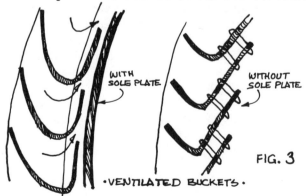

WITH
SOLE PLATE

WITHOUT
SOLE PLATE

FIG. 3

·VENTILATED BUCKETS·

and a maximum velocity of seven feet per second is standard for falls five or six feet. In general, the higher the fall, the slower the edge speed, and vice versa; the formula is s equals 7.44 h (.088) where s is speed in feet per second, and h is height of fall in feet.

Wheel Buckets: Bucket aperture is the narrowest distance between buckets measured perpendicularly to the direction in which the water enters the wheel. Bucket aperture varies according to how high up on the wheel the water enters. The aperture should be from five and a half to eight inches for high breast wheels, and from 9 to 12 inches for low breast wheels. Note: Bucket aperture is different from bucket spacing.

The area of opening of the buckets is the product of bucket aperture times the length between the shroud (inside width of wheel). For overshot and high breast wheels, one square foot area of opening per five cubic feet of bucket capacity is usual; for breast wheels which receive water at a height of not more than 10 degrees above the horizontal diameter, one square foot area of opening per three cubic feet of bucket capacity is usual. With these proportions, the depth of the shrouding (depth of bucket toward centre of the wheel) is assumed to be about two to two and a half times the bucket aperture.

The spacing of buckets, or their distance apart, should be from one to one and a half feet. The approximate formula is n equals 2.5d, where n is the number of buckets, and d is the diameter of the wheel.

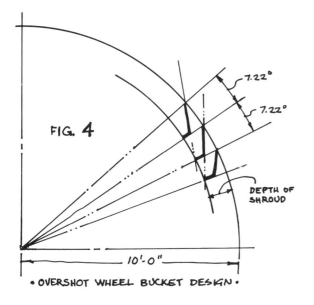

FIG. 4

7.22°
7.22°

DEPTH OF SHROUD

10'-0"

• OVERSHOT WHEEL BUCKET DESIGN •

The shape of buckets is important to the operation of the wheel. The ideal shape is a curvilinear one, but often it is more practical to approximate the ideal with straight sections. For overshot wheels (fig. 4), a convenient method for determining the bucket shape is to draw one radius inclined 34° from the horizontal, and a second radius exactly one bucket arc (determined from the computed number of buckets on the wheel) below it; if a vertical line is drawn through the point determined by outer edge

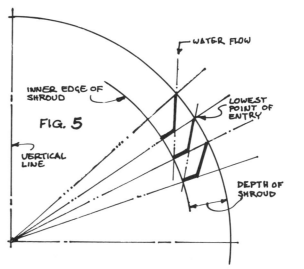

WATER FLOW

INNER EDGE OF SHROUD

FIG. 5

LOWEST POINT OF ENTRY

VERTICAL LINE

DEPTH OF SHROUD

• BREAST WHEEL BUCKET DESIGN •

of the wheel and the first radius, then the bucket shape is defined by the vertical line and the second radius. The depth of the shrouds (the shrouds are the outer sides of the buckets — they determine the depth of the buckets, measured towards the centre of the wheel) is usually twice the bucket aperture (bucket aperture being the smallest dimension between buckets, and not bucket spacing).

The shape of the buckets for breast wheels is determined slightly differently. The wheel is planned so that the point and angle at which water enters the wheel is known; entry should be nearly tangential. Since the breast of a breast wheel is designed to keep the water on the wheel, the bucket shape need not be designed to hold water all the way to the bottom; therefore, the bucket shape (fig. 5) is planned to allow maximum ease of water entry, which means that the initial angle of entry of water determines the shape of the bucket. To be precise, a line is drawn from the bottom edge of the feed trough in the direction of water flow to the wheel. Through the point where this flow line intersects the outside edge of the wheel, draw a radius. Draw a second radius exactly one bucket arc (determined from the computed number of buckets on the wheel) below it. The bucket shape is then defined by the flow line and the second radius. The depth of the bucket is again two to two and a half times the bucket aperture.

Design Computations: The design of a water wheel is done according to the following steps. First the height of fall, and the volume of flow of the stream are determined. The amount of power available can then be computed. Next, the type of wheel should be selected: overshot wheels are easier to build, breast wheels can use lower falls. The selection of wheel will determine its diameter. The form of bucket is next determined. The computed edge speed of the wheel, and the volume flow of the stream, will determine the volume capacity of the bucket necessary. (Note: The buckets should never be more than 1/3 to 1/2 filled). The volume capacity of the buckets will fix the necessary breadth (width) of the wheel.

As an example, suppose you have a little stream (30 inches wide and 6-1/2 inches deep) with a flow of 200 cu. feet per min. which has a head of 20 feet. This makes 7.87 horsepower (for power calculations, see page 40) available. If you wish to build an overshot wheel on this creek (it's the simplest to build), the diameter of the wheel will be 20 feet.

The number of buckets is n equals 2.5 (20) equals 50 buckets; one bucket arc equals 360/50 equals 7.22 degrees. From the geometry of the wheel, it is determined that the depth of shroud is about 1.12 feet or 12-3/4 inches. The distance between buckets equals the circumference of the wheel divided by 50 equals 20 pi/50 equals 1.25 feet per bucket. The edge speed of the wheel is s equals 7.44 - 20(.088) equals 5.69 feet per second.

Therefore the number of buckets which pass the feed sluice per second is the edge speed divided by the bucket spacing: 5.69 feet per second divided by 1.25 feet per bucket equals 4.55 buckets per second. The volume flow of the stream is 200 cubic feet per minute, which equals 3.33 cubic feet per second. Therefore, the amount of water each bucket must hold is the volume flow of the stream divided by the number of buckets per second, which is 3.3 cubic feet per second divided by 4.55 buckets per second, equals .69 cubic feet per bucket. The sectional area of each bucket is the area of the wheel minus the area of the wheel to the bottom of the buckets, divided by 50 buckets: (pi x 10 squared minus pi x 8.98 squared) divided by 50 equals (314 - 254) divided by 50 equals 1.2 square feet. Therefore the breadth of the wheel must be volume of the bucket divided by the sectional area equals .69 cubic feet per bucket divided by 1.2 square feet per bucket equals .572 feet wheel width. Since each bucket must be only 1/2 to 1/3 full, the breadth of the wheel should really be about 1-1/2 feet.

Checking the geometry, the bucket aperture is about 5 inches (assuming 1/2 inch thickness of wood in the bucket). The aperture times the wheel breadth equals about .6 square feet opening per 2 cubic feet total bucket volume, which is the same as 1 square foot bucket opening per 3.3 cubic feet bucket volume. Therefore the area

of opening of the bucket is rather larger than the ideal, 1 square foot to 5 cubic feet volume. This means that the outer boards of the bucket should be larger and closer to back of the preceding bucket. This would both decrease the area of opening, and help retain the water on the wheel for a longer time.

Undershot Wheels

A well designed low breast wheel is, in effect, an undershot wheel. It is of course, a gravity wheel, because the weight of the water causes the wheel to turn. There is another class of undershot wheels which are called impulse wheels, because it is the velocity of the water striking the wheel which causes it to turn. The conceptual ideal of an impulse wheel is to extract all the kinetic energy from moving water, reducing the forward velocity of the water to zero, and afterward letting it drain vertically downward. For this to happen, the edge speed of the wheel must be one-half the velocity of the water.

Primitive impulse undershot wheels were very imperfect in this respect, as the speed of the tailrace was considerable. The Poncelet wheel (fig. 6), however, is quite effective, being as good or better than a low breast wheel, and giving efficiencies of better than 60 per cent.

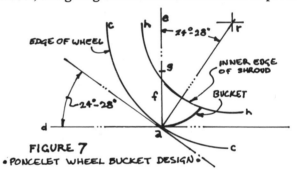

FIGURE 7
• PONCELET WHEEL BUCKET DESIGN •

The buckets on a Poncelet (fig. 7) wheel are curved, and open toward the interior of the wheel. To lay out the shape of the buckets, draw an arc cc as part of the external circumference of the wheel, and draw ar to be the radius of the wheel. Let ab equal 1/3 to 1/4 the height of fall, and draw hh as the inner circumference of the shrouding. Let the water first strike the bucket at the point a, from the direction da, so that the angle ear will be from 24 degrees to 28 degrees. On the line ae, draw fg equals 1/6 af. From the centre g, with a radius ga, draw an arc from point a to the inner edge of the shroud; this arc describes the shape of a Poncelet wheel bucket. With less efficiency, this shape may approximated with two or three straight boards.

The number of buckets on the wheel is determined by the formula n equals 8/5d plus 16, where n is the number of buckets, and d is the diameter of the wheel. The velocity of the water entering the wheel may be approximated by measuring the volume flow into the wheel (upstream) in cubic feet per minute and dividing this by the area of the opening to the wheel in feet squared, yielding an answer in feet per minute water speed. To obtain maximum power from the wheel, the edge speed of the wheel must be one-half the water velocity.

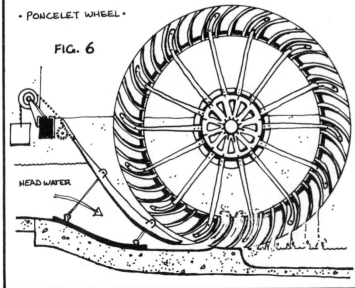

• PONCELET WHEEL •

FIG. 6

HEAD WATER

The bottom 18 to 20 incheds of the wheel must be very carefully fitted to the race for efficient operation. Also, the tailrace should expand in width and depth to keep the wheel clear of backwater.

The wheel shown in the figure was 16 feet 8 inches in diameter, and 30 feet wide, and was driven by a fall 6 feet 6 inches high, yielding 20,000 cubic feet per minute. With an edge speed of 11 to 12 feet per second, the wheel produced 140 horsepower.

Construction of Wheels

Since the speed of water wheels is generally low, they tend to deliver power at high torque; therefore, the axle of the wheel must be very strong. The six-horsepower overshot wheel in the previous example will deliver five or six times the torque of an automobile engine. Therefore a large wooden beam (railroad tie) or tractor axle will be necessary. One method of avoiding torque problems and getting higher shaft speeds is to take power from the outer edge of the wheel; this was usually done with cogs, which are not common today. So it is tricky mechanically.

All gravity wheels must be very strongly built, as they must support the weight of the water on the wheel. Poncelet wheels may be lighter in construction, since they do not support any water weight.

There are two basic methods of wheel construction. The first is to have the spokes of the wheel support weight by compression. The second is to have the spokes support the wheel by tension; a wheel of this type was built with chains as spokes — but this is not recommended. Most wheels operate on a combination of these principles.

New Work: My researches in water wheels have led me to several new design ideas. The first is a valve ventilated overshot wheel. This would allow the bucket openings to be much smaller, while having the buckets fill more quickly and empty later, and thus keep the water on the wheel longer. Simple plastic flap valves might work well. A second design I've been working on is an impulse wheel, midway in head and volume flow between the Poncelet wheel and the Pelton wheel. This wheel would handle heads of about 20 to 50 feet in the form of waterfalls. This would allow small-diameter high-speed wheels to be used, without expensive feed pipes.

Finally, I have been working on an impulse wheel design which will accept water near the centre of the wheel, rather than tangentially. This would increase the speed of the wheel, making it more useful for electrical power generation.

Another device I have designed and built working models of is a "constant flow sluice." This sluice has a constant outflow of water, no matter how much the input changes (above a certain minimum). The sluice is useful in situations where only a small portion of a rather large flow is needed and under low head conditions (for instance, feeding a Michell turbine). The regulation of water flow is accomplished by a low dam with a very low

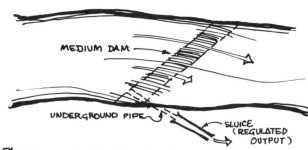

· PLAN VIEW OF CONSTANT FLOW SLUICE WITH A SINGLE STAGE OF REGULATION ·

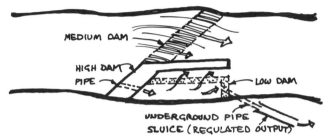

· PLAN VIEW OF CONSTANT FLOW SLUICE WITH TWO STAGES OF REGULATION ·

FIGURE 9

level to several inches above normal stream level. Most of the water flows over the dam, but the sluice later is taken from a pipe under the dam. This sluice water can be regulated again by a second small dam lower than the first. The advantages of the sluice are that it requires no adjustments, and that it is easy to build.

If anyone wishes to work on these or other new designs, please contact me at address below.

Assistance: If anyone needs help on the design or installation of a water wheel, I will be glad to assist. Contact by mail to:

Guy Immega
General Delivery
Lasquiti Island
British Columbia
Canada

Bibliography

Mills and Millwork
by Sir William Fairbairn
Longmans, Green and Co.
London, England
1888.

*Power Development of
Small Streams*
by Carl C. Harris and
Samuel O. Rice

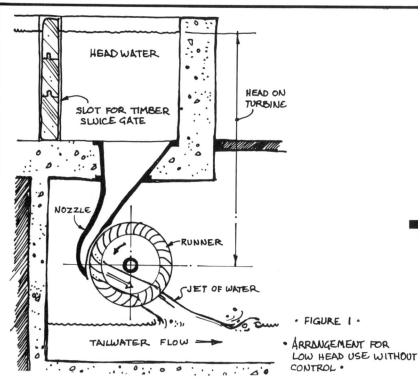

HEAD WATER

SLOT FOR TIMBER SLUICE GATE

HEAD ON TURBINE

NOZZLE

RUNNER

JET OF WATER

TAILWATER FLOW →

· FIGURE 1 ·

· ARRANGEMENT FOR LOW HEAD USE WITHOUT CONTROL ·

The Michell Turbine

The Michell (or Banki) turbine is simple in construction. Welding equipment and a small machine shop like those often used to repair farm machinery and automotive parts are all that is necessary.

The two main parts of the Michell turbine are the runner and the nozzle. Both are welded from plate steel and require some machining. Figures 1 and 2 show the arrangement of a turbine of this type for low-head use without control. This installation drives a direct-current generator with a belt drive. Because the construction can be a do-it-yourself project, formulas and design details are given for a runner of 12'' outside diameter. This size is the smallest which is easy to fabricate and weld. It has a wide range of application for all small power developments with head and flow suitable for the Michell turbine. Different heads result in different rotational speeds. The proper belt drive ratio gives the correct generator speed. Various amounts of water determine the width of the nozzle (B1, figure 2) and the width of the runner (B2, figure 2). These widths may vary from 2'' to 14''. No other turbine is adaptable to as large a range of flow. The water passes through the runner twice in a narrow jet before discharge into the tailrace. The runner consists of two side plates, each 14'' thick with hubs for the shaft attached by welding, and from 20 to 24 blades. Each blade is 0.237'' thick and cut from 4'' standard pipe. Steel pipe of this type is available virtually everywhere. A pipe of suitable length produces four blades. Each blade is a circular segment with a centre angle of 72 degrees. The runner design, with dimensions for a foot-long runner, is shown in figure 3; and figure 4 gives the nozzle design and dimensions. The dimensions can be altered proportionally for other size runners. Upstream from the nozzle discharge opening of 1-1/4,'' the shape of the nozzle can be made to suit penstock pipe conditions.

To calculate the principal turbine dimensions:

(B1)=Width of Nozzle (inches)

$$= \frac{210 \times \text{Flow (cubic feet per second)}}{\text{Runner outside diameter (inches} \times \sqrt{\text{Head (feet)}}}$$

(B2)=Width of Runner between Discs
=(B1)+1.0''

Rotational Speed (rpm)

$$= \frac{862 \times \text{Head (feet)}}{\text{Runner outside diameter (in.)}}$$

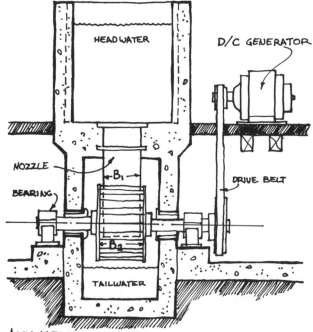

HEAD WATER

D/C GENERATOR

NOZZLE

B_1

BEARING

B_2

DRIVE BELT

TAILWATER

· ARRANGEMENT OF A MITCHELL (BANKI) TURBINE FOR LOW HEAD USE WITHOUT CONTROL (B) ·

FIGURE 2

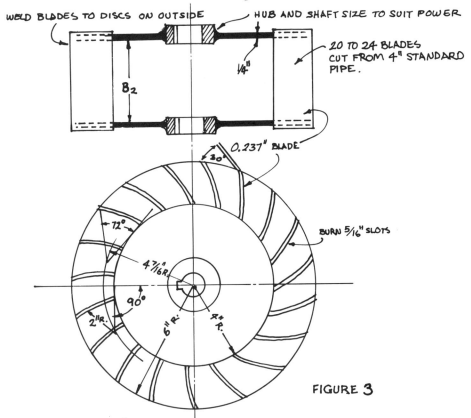

WELD BLADES TO DISCS ON OUTSIDE

HUB AND SHAFT SIZE TO SUIT POWER

B_2

1/4"

20 TO 24 BLADES CUT FROM 4" STANDARD PIPE.

0.237" BLADE

30

72°

4 7/16 R.

90°

2" R.

6" R.

4" R.

BURN 5/16" SLOTS

FIGURE 3

• DETAIL OF 12" DIAMETER MITCHELL RUNNER •

The efficiency of the Michell turbine is 80 per cent or greater and, therefore, suitable for small power installations. Flow regulation and governor control of the flow can be effected by using a centre-body nozzle regulator (a closing mechanism in the shape of a gate in the nozzle). This is expensive because of governor costs. It is, however, needed for running an alternating-current generator.

The application of figures 1 and 2 is a typical example. For high heads the Michell turbine is connected to a penstock with a turbine inlet valve. This requires a different type of arrangement from the one shown here. As mentioned before, the Michell turbine is unique because its B1 and B2 widths can be altered to suit power-site traits of flow rate and head. This, besides simplicity and low cost, makes it the most suitable of all water turbines for small power developments.

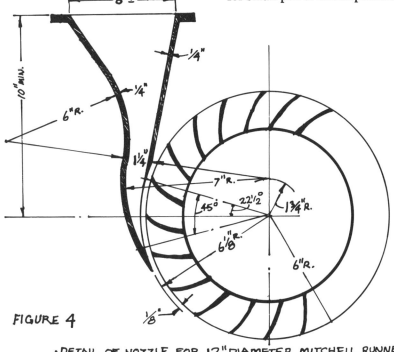

6"±

10" MIN.

1/4"

1/4"

6" R.

1 1/4"

7" R.

45°

22 1/2°

1 3/4" R.

6 1/8" R.

6" R.

1/8"

FIGURE 4

• DETAIL OF NOZZLE FOR 12" DIAMETER MITCHELL RUNNER •

A Wooden Undershot Wheel

by Glen Bass

We divided the construction of the water wheel into three parts: the dam, the trough (or millrace), and the wheel.

The Dam

We used a beaver-type dam. Beavers are very experienced hydraulic engineers. You would be wise to invest some time in studying their methods, if you are going to mess around with a stream. You'll also have to get a power permit and water permit from the local water board.

The first thing we built was the *pier,* which is a log foundation that is embedded in one bank of the stream and lends support to the water wheel. The logs were all pre-cut, numbered, and notched, and then assembled to form the cubic structure which is illustrated in figure 1. In this structure, one side of the cube was left out, and the ends of the logs were embedded sideways into the stream bed with dirt and rocks. It was then filled with more rocks.

Next we built the *pylon.* That was assembled just like the pier, only it was a complete cube. Also, the pylon sits midstream. To install it in the stream, we laced heavy wire across the bottom of the cube to make a basket for the first layer of rocks. Then we floated the structure into position and sank it with rocks (see figure 1). In order to avoid some heavy lifting, it would be easier to assemble just the base of the pylon first, or as many layers as you can carry into the stream from the bank, then position it in the stream, and add the first layer of rocks, and so on. The top layer of the pylon was foreshortened slightly (see figure 2) to provide a base for the support

log, which extended from the pylon to the opposite bank of the stream (see figure 1). This is the backbone of the dam, so use good material. We chose a white pine log, very strong, not too heavy, and it was close to the site. To install the support log, we had to make sure that both ends of the log were secured; the end resting on the bank we secured with dirt and rock, and the end which rested on the pylon was secured with wire.

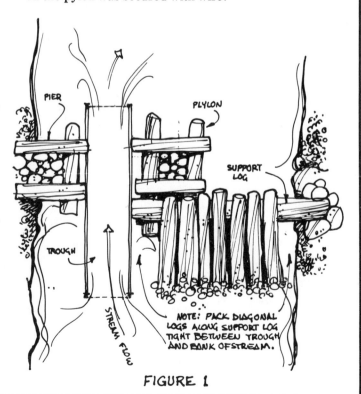

NOTE: PACK DIAGONAL LOGS ALONG SUPPORT LOG TIGHT BETWEEN TROUGH AND BANK OF STREAM.

FIGURE 1

Now we were ready to close the dam. This was actually the very last step in assembling the water wheel, but we did it at this point in order to test the structure before setting the wheel in place. Once the strength of the structure had been tested, the damming, which was composed of brush and support logs, was disassembled and then assembled again later. It was an extra day's work, but it saved us a lot of trouble later.

As in any project, certain steps *must* precede others. *Before closing the dam,* the trough had to be placed between the pier and the pylon, otherwise the rushing water would cut a huge hole in the stream bed, undercut the pier and the pylon, and mess up the whole thing. The trough served to channel the water over wood, rather than over the bottom of the stream, so there was no washing away of stream bottom.

Our next step was to cut a number of small logs. They had to be long enough so that one end of the small log leaned against the support log, while the other end of the small log was embedded in the stream bed and extended out against the current at an angle of 45 degrees relative to the bottom (see figure 2). The small logs were then placed as close together as possible, leaning in a line along the support log (see figure 1). They were not nailed in place. Their placement at a 45-degree angle in relation to the stream bottom distributed the pressure of the rushing water half onto the logs and half onto the stream bed itself. When all the logs were in place, the force of the water held them securely.

To complete the dam, we caulked the logs with lots of bark, brush, old hay, whatever was lying around. When doing this, however, we had to allow for the appropriate water level. We layered the packing to a level below the walls of the trough, so that when there's an overflow the water doesn't flow into the trough, but rather flows over the dam into the stream. We then placed a sheet of plastic over the packing, anchoring it at the bottom with rocks. It extended from the proposed water level down to the base of the dam and *out into the stream bed at least 2 ft.* (see figure 2). Again, the force of the

water holds the material. The packing supports the plastic so that it does not balloon out between the logs. The plastic on the stream bed in front of the dam prevents undercutting. Also, the plastic was placed so that when the dam filled, the excess water, if any, passed readily between the logs above the plastic thus forming a natural spillway.

The Trough

The construction of the wheel consists of two parts: the trough or millrace and the actual wheel. The trough is not absolutely necessary, but greatly increases the efficiency of the unit (by approximately 70 per cent).

Here I must try to explain a little about what you are trying to do, instead of how to do it. A stream may be viewed as matter (water) or as a *stream of energy.* The object is to convert some of this energy from linear motion to rotary motion. We describe the energy of the stream as either actual or potential. The actual energy is the tendency of elevated water to seek sea level, i.e. gravity. By constructing the dam, we accomplished two things: we "backed up" the stream or elevated it, and we channelled the motion into a place that would serve our purposes (the trough).

In constructing the trough, we had to plan it so that the wheel would fit closely inside it, allowing at least 1 in. clearance on each side. We decided to build the trough 4 ft. wide, based on equations from a textbook on hydraulics. Similar equations can be found on page 59. The trough had to be long enough to accommodate the wheel and also a gate at the front (see figures 3 and 4). The purpose of the gate was to control the flow of water through the trough in order to regulate the speed of the turning wheel. Also, the tail end of the trough had to be long enough to release the water smoothly and prevent undercutting of the stream bed in that area.

The floor of the trough has a *dish* into which the wheel fits. The size of the dish was determined as follows. We did all our plans to full scale with nails and

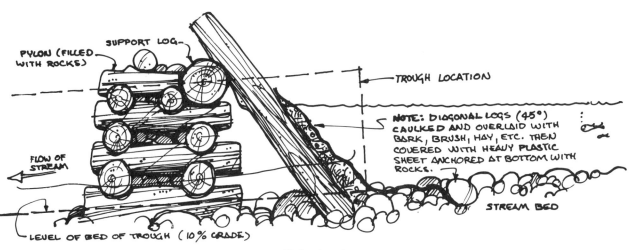

FIGURE 2

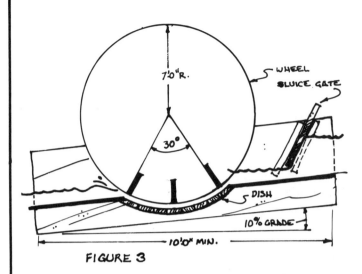

FIGURE 3

string on the floor to avoid math errors. Draw an arc using the radius of the wheel (7 ft. in our case). Next draw a 30-degree angle, with the apex at the centre point. Where the legs of the angle cross the arc, draw a line. This line is in alignment with the flow of the trough, and the arc is the dish. In our trough, the dish was 4 in. deep. The 30-degree angle is important, because the paddles of the wheel will be spaced 15 degrees apart. This means that as one paddle is entering the dish, another is at mid-point in the dish, and a third is at the exit point. This provides a smooth motion to the wheel.

We used 3/4-in. marine grade plywood, leaving space for the dish, of course. The floor of the dish was constructed of 2 x 4's nailed crossways in between the plywood walls (also 3/4-in. marine grade) of the trough.

Before we installed the trough between the pier and pylon, we had to erect a structure to support the shaft of the wheel. We used two 18-ft. 2 x 6's on each side and installed them so that they were flush with the sides of the pier and pylon (see figure 4). The 2 x 6's extended well above the wheel and were tied together by a platform above the wheel. The cross support for the wheel shaft was made with a piece of 8-in. x 2 1/2-in. stock (see figure 4).

After this was completed, we nailed the trough in place between the pier and pylon. The floor of the trough was set at a 10 per cent grade relative to the level of water behind the dam. For example, a 10-ft. trough would be set at the same level as the water level behind the dam (see figure 3).

Remember that the shaft must be above the centre line of the "dish." Since the trough is placed on a grade, the actual centre line A-C will be slightly behind the apparent centre line A-B.

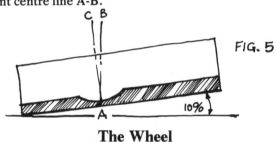

FIG. 5

The Wheel

We started with an 8-in. x 8-in. x 7-ft. beam. For bearings, we used two large ball-bearings salvaged from the scrap bin of a heavy equipment repair shop, about 9 in. in diameter (see figure 6). The ends of the shaft were rounded to accept the bearings.

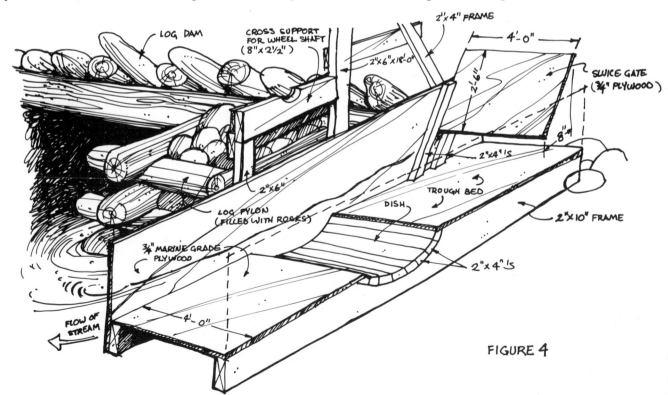

FIGURE 4

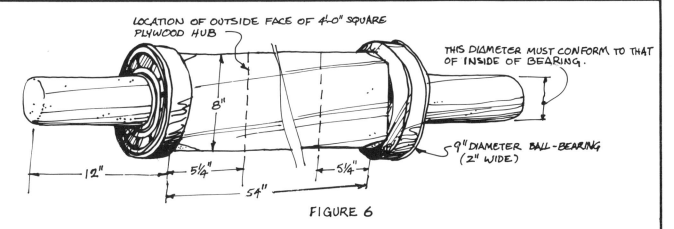

FIGURE 6

In order to fix the spokes of the wheel to the shaft, we bought a 4-ft. x 8-ft. x 3/4-in. sheet of marine grade plywood and cut it into 4-ft. x 4-ft. squares. Then we cut an 8-in. square hole in the centre of each piece. Before cutting the 8-in. hole, we found the centre point and drew a large circle on the plywood, and then we divided the circle into 30-degree segments (see figure 8). These 30-degree lines were the centre lines for the spokes. Next we fixed the plywood to the shaft. Figure 7 illustrates how we did this. First, we inserted the rounded end of the shaft through the hole in the plywood, so that the square edges in both parts were lined up, and then we fastened the plywood square onto the square part of the shaft end, using four 2 x 4's (refer to figure 6 for detail of the shaft end(. We used waterproof glue and ardox twist nails for all joints.

After this, we mounted the shaft on the cross support and aligned it to make sure it was true. Then we attached 12 6-ft. 2 x 4's to each plywood plate, using glue and bolts (see figure 9). By building the wheel in place, we were able to check the alignment constantly as we worked.

To join the ends of the spokes around the circumference of the wheel, we used 1-in. x 12-in. stock. On our wheel, the distance between the spokes at the circumference was 44 in.. After the stock was attached, we rounded the outer edges.

Next we added the paddles. There were 12 paddles that were affixed to the 12 spokes, and another 12 paddles that were affixed between the spokes. The paddles

affixed to the spokes consisted of two boards spanning the width of the wheel. Board 1 (see figure 9) was advanced 2 in. into the flow of the water by means of a small wedge attached to the end of each spoke, and board 2 was attached above board 1, but flush with the spoke. This created a scooping kind of paddle. The paddle affixed between the spokes was just one board and was attached to the 1-in. x 12-in. stock that was used to join the ends of the spokes around the circumference of the wheel (see board 2, fig. 9). Board 3 had to be aligned at the same angle as board 1, i.e., in relation to an imaginary spoke drawn from the centre of the wheel to the 1'' x 12'' piece of stock adjoining the spokes. If the water flows over board 3 rather than being cupped by it, another board similar to board 2 may be attached above it to make another scooping paddle (board 4, fig. 9). Ideally the paddles would be made of curved sheet metal (with a radius of 1 ft.), but because they would have cost $3.00 for each blade, we used wood.

Our wheel turns at 20 r.p.m. and generates an estimated 3 hp. Now we are looking for a water pump to complete the system. Our future plan is to build a long workshop parallel to the shaft of the wheel, with a high-speed metal shaft running the length of the shop. Attached to the shaft we plan a deep-freeze (with motor removed), a wringer washer, a 12-volt generator, a small wood lathe, and a flour mill.

We face two problems in operating this system: (a) ice in winter; (b) high water. Removing some logs from the dam should take care of the spring flood. The ice

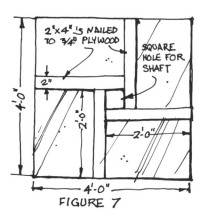

FIGURE 7

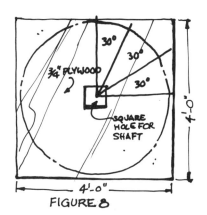

FIGURE 8

problem we will work out when it comes. Perhaps enclosing the entire structure in a shed will solve this.

Generally we used good material throughout and spent $130.00 on lumber, nails, glue, etc.

Aside from the fact that we feel the wheel will be a dependable (and cheap) power source, the project has given us all a new sense of what energy is and how it is related to our lives.

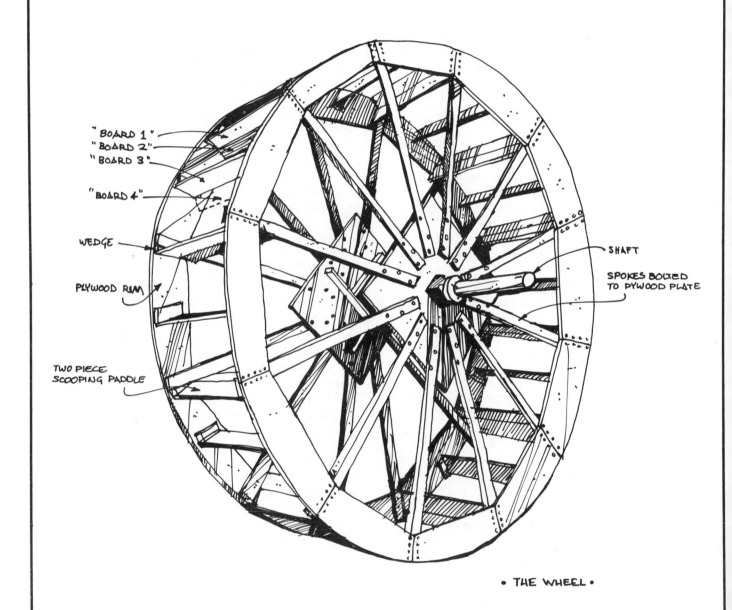

"BOARD 1"
"BOARD 2"
"BOARD 3"
"BOARD 4"
WEDGE
PLYWOOD RIM
TWO PIECE SCOOPING PADDLE
SHAFT
SPOKES BOLTED TO PYWOOD PLATE

• THE WHEEL •

FIGURE 9

by Don Gilmour

A Wooden Overshot Wheel

If you wish to build an overshot wheel, the first thing would be to measure the available power by the amount of water flowing and the distance of fall. The directions for this can be found from pages 42 to 51.

My wheel has been running continuously for two years without added lubrication or trouble. It's simply designed and easily constructed with a minimal outlay of money. With a bit of hunting for used materials, you should be able to build it for very little money.

After measuring your available power, refer to page 56 for the best dimensions to construct your wheel. The construction requires the manufacture of five basic parts: the disc, the shrouds, the buckets, the mounting framework, and the pulleys.

The Disc

To make the disc, saw out of 5/8'' plywood a circle 44'' in diameter, and mark the centre. Now nail small sections of 1'' x 2'' on the sides, all around the rim. These pieces should be cut to the same radius or curvature as the rim of the disc. Do this on both sides. The object is to thicken the rim. Now cut a 4' x 8' sheet of 1/4'' plywood into strips 15'' wide. Bend the strips to that they overhang on the disc equally. Nail all around the rim like a wide tire. Nail a second layer over this, staggering the joints from the first layer to give added strength and tightness.

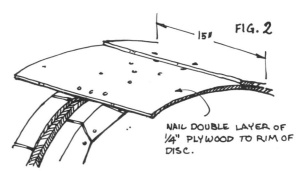

NAIL DOUBLE LAYER OF 1/4" PLYWOOD TO RIM OF DISC.

FIG. 2

The Shroud

The shrouds close in the sides of the bucket (see figure 3). Attaching the shrouds increases the wheel diameter to approximately 5'.

To construct them, cut pieces of cedar lumber into sections to match the cardboard pattern, which is designed as follows:

Take a yardstick or equivalent size piece of wood and drive a nail through one end of it and into the floor. Measure 22-1/2'' from this nail and drive another nail through the yardstick only. Use this ''compass'' to scribe the two curved lines (figure 3) for the shroud pattern. Make the shroud pattern long enough to efficiently utilize the wood you have available. My lumber was 11'' x 7/8'' cedar stock.

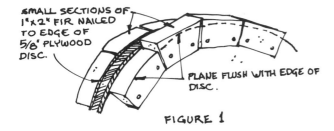

SMALL SECTIONS OF 1"X2" FIR NAILED TO EDGE OF 5/8' PLYWOOD DISC.

PLANE FLUSH WITH EDGE OF DISC.

FIGURE 1

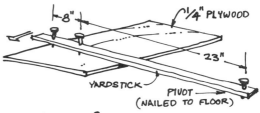

1/4" PLYWOOD

YARDSTICK

PIVOT (NAILED TO FLOOR)

23"

8"

FIGURE 3

Nails are driven through the double plywood rim into the edge of the shrouds to fasten them in place. A second set of shrouds made from the same pattern is constructed of 1/4'' plywood. They are nailed on the outside of the original shroud, in such a way as to cover the seam between shrouds; it also adds strength and increases water tightness. The neater and tighter the better.

The wheel should look something like a giant spool. You can butter up the cracks with any suitable asphalt roof patching compound or waterproof crack sealer.

The Buckets

The 12 buckets are made from fir. They are assembled and the two parts of each are nailed together on a bench, before installing between the shrouds. Measure the distance between the shrouds and make the buckets to fit neatly between, so they will stay reasonably watertight. The water inlet trough should be narrower than the wheel, with up to 10'' high sides.

Mark the location of each bucket on the wheel, so they come out similarly spaced. Use your judging faculties and divide up the spacing.

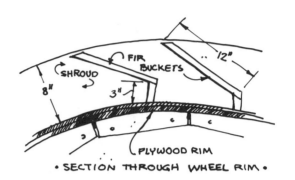

· SECTION THROUGH WHEEL RIM ·

FIGURE 4

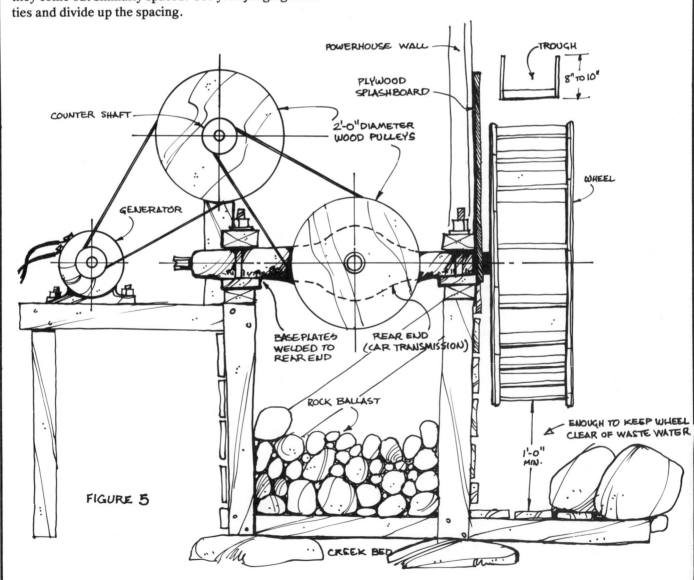

FIGURE 5

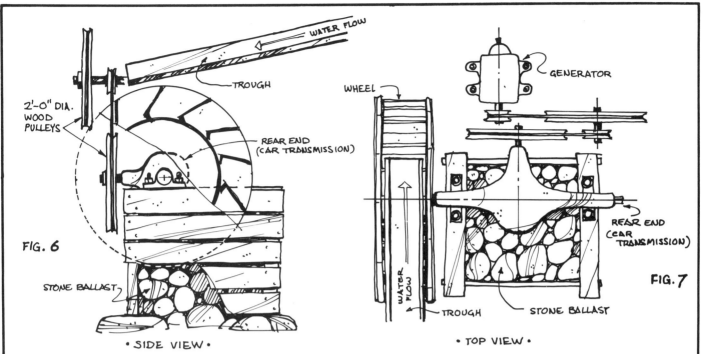

FIG. 6

2'-0" DIA. WOOD PULLEYS

TROUGH

WATER FLOW

REAR END (CAR TRANSMISSION)

STONE BALLAST

· SIDE VIEW ·

WHEEL

GENERATOR

REAR END (CAR TRANSMISSION)

FIG. 7

WATER FLOW

TROUGH

STONE BALLAST

· TOP VIEW ·

Mounting the Wheel

Take a rear end from a full-sized car and fix the differential gears, so the two axles turn as one unit. You can jam these gears by welding or otherwise, so they don't operate. Cut off one axle and the axle housing to get rid of the brake assembly, if you wish. The other axle should be cleaned of brake parts to expose the hub and flange. You may have to knock the bolts out and get rid of the brake drum. The wooden disc of the water wheel needs to have a hole made in its centre to closely fit the car wheel hub. Also it should be drilled to match the old bolt holes, and bolts installed with washers under the nuts.

Before mounting the wheel in place, have a base plate welded to the axle housing. It should be on what is to be the underside, with two holes for 1/2" lagscrews, or do it your own way. Make some kind of anchor to hold the opposite housing from moving around.

If you want to do it pioneer style, then hew poles square or use 4 x 4's for the framework, as in the illustration. Install the rear end in place, using lagscrews or bolts to hold it. Install the wheel.

Pulleys

Make two pulleys from 5/8" plywood and nail sections of 1" cedar or fir lumber on one side of the rim to widen it. These are for belt pulleys. Bolt one of them centrally onto the flange from which you removed the car drive (torque) shaft. The second pulley goes on the countershaft with a 6" x 5/8" V-pulley alongside it. See what you can scrounge up. The important thing is to get the 2' and 6" pulleys turning as a unit and on some kind of bearings such as auto front wheels. If you make your counter shaft of grease-sealed ball or roller-type bearings, you should have a more efficient or carefree plant.

There should be a gate to stop the water from flowing in the trough, thereby controlling the speed or shutting the wheel off. It can be made to slide over the end of

the trough, if the butts of planks are nice and square. It operates in the manner of a gate valve.

At first run, the wood pulley can be turned true and the rim given a slight crown (rounded groove) which helps the belt stay on. Install the countershaft, fitting the V-belt from the 2' pulley to the 6" V-pulley on the countershaft. When the countershaft is running O K. turn the rim of its pulley and crown a little. The turning operation needs care to avoid accidents. Use a long-handled chisel or scraper. One needs a firm support under the tool to operate in a manner similar to a wood lathe. A V-groove in these pulleys will wear the belt away. The slightly-crowned wood face works for years without noticeable wear.

The second belt goes from countershaft wooden pulley to the generator metal V-pulley or whatever you wish to drive. A 4" pulley will be easy on the belt and give you about 1800 r.p.m. The wood pulley on countershaft can be larger diameter for greater speed.

A car generator will give you a fine lighting system, if you put the battery at the house end of the line. Use No.8 wire for a distance of 50' to 100' and beyond that, No. 6 wire. The generator will build up extra voltage to overcome the normal voltage drop in the line. Fifty-watt bulbs are still available in 6 and 12 volts. You may still be able to find 100-watt bulbs for 6 or 12-volt systems. The bases are the same standard screw as the 110-volt bulbs, so they fit standard light fixtures. A 32-volt battery system is still better than a 12-volt system.

You can get up to 500 watts of 110 volt A.C. from this wheel with an efficient, self-regulating, four-pole alternator, but it will be difficult to keep close to 60 cycles unless the load is unchanging. You won't be able to store power as you can on a battery system.

Log dams and all the woodwork which keeps wet will last for years. Parts of the wheel that are exposed to the elements should be coated with a preservative.

Frost Damage Prevention

by M.G. Kains

The killing of plants and plant parts by frost may often be prevented by simple, inexpensive, easily applied means.

Frost is the term which indicates the conversion of a liquid into a solid by the reduction of temperature. Though this definition covers all cases, such as the solidification of molten iron and other metals, it is popularly understood to mean the formation of ice from water at the temperature of 32°F.

As air cools, its power to hold water in vapour form decreases, until it is deposited in tiny drops (dew) on objects cooler than itself, such as foliage. The temperatures at which this deposition occurs depend upon the proportion of water vapour in the air at the time. This varies as the cooling proceeds. During summer, the dew point, as the deposition or saturation temperature is called, is often above 60°F.; in winter, often below 0°F.

When the dew point is below the freezing point, the water vapour condenses on still cooler surfaces in the form of fine particles of ice, which, because they reflect the sunlight and appear white, we call hoar or white frost. Often a similar appearance of "false hoar frost" occurs when the temperature is several degrees above freezing point. Usually this is due to the way the light is reflected from the dew.

The condensation of water vapour tends to check the fall of temperature, because what is called "latent heat" in this vapour is returned to the air, which becomes measurably warmer. Thus, within variable limits, the position of dew protects plants from frost damage as the temperature approaches or in some cases even goes below the freezing point. This accounts for many escapes of plants that would have been killed by frost, had the dew point been below instead of above the freezing point. You can often take advantage of this phenomenon and save your plants.

Plants vary in their resistance to frost damage, according to their origin and their condition. Those which originate in a cold climate (apple, cabbage) naturally are strongly resistant; those from a warm climate (orange, tomato) are weak and easily destroyed. Between these extremes are many intermediate grades. Those plants that, in a given locality, live through the northern or alpine winter in spite of deep freezing of the soil, are called hardy in that locality; those that succumb to the slightest frost are tender, and those between are variously classed as half-hardy, semi-hardy, half-tender, and semi-tender (e.g., French artichoke).

Tender plants are usually injured when the temperature continues at 32°F., 31°F., or 30°F. for several hours, especially when bright sunshine or quickly warming air strikes them in early morning. Few if any of them can stand lower degrees than these for even a short time; half-hardy plants often survive temperatures of 20°F., but seldom lower degrees.

In all these cases, plant condition plays an important part; for plants that have made rapid growth have soft, immature tissues and are full of water, are far less resistant than those which have developed slowly, have denser, stockier growth, and are less full (perhaps even in need of) water. This statement applies to hardy as well as tender plants; even trees normally hardy in a given locality may be winter-killed because they made a late, sappy growth which did not ripen or which was full of water when cold weather arrived.

The mere deposition of frost on the surface of foliage does not necessarily indicate that the plants have been killed or even damaged. But when the air is too dry for dew to be deposited, they may be frozen by a dry wind, or on a clear night without the deposition of either dew or hoar frost. In such cases damage is due to freezing of the water inside the plant and the consequent rupture of the

tissues. When the sun shines on tissues thus injured, the internal ice melts; the leaves have no chance to mend the broken cells, so the leaves droop, wilt, and turn back; hence the term "black frost."

Anything that will prevent the fall of temperature to or below the freezing point and anything that will shield the plants from direct sunshine while they are still frozen, covered with hoar frost, or severely chilled, will help ward off damage or even save plants that would otherwise die or be seriously checked in their development. A wind that springs up in the evening, clouds that appear during the night or early morning, or a rain that follows a frost will often either prevent the freezing or check the thawing process and thus save the plants. All these phenomena of nature are, of course, beyond your control, but you may imitate them, as outlined further on.

You can largely control the development and therefore the hardiness of your plants in several ways. For instance, during spring you can avoid over-feeding your young plants with stimulant fertilizer, such as manure, and also avoid giving them excess of water. Both these tend to make sappy growth easily killed by frost. On the other hand, by keeping the plants cool, almost cold ("hardening them off") as they approach the time for transplanting to the open ground, you can increase the hardiness of hardy, semi-hardy, and even tender plants. Plants so prepared will stand cold snaps, whereas those of the same species not so inured would probalby be killed or so chilled that they would "sulk" for several weeks before recovering or renewing a normal rate of growth.

Similarly we may prevent winter injury of hardy trees, shrubs and vines, by supplying ample water during summer and early autumn, witholding it later; avoid application of manures from midsummer forward; counteracting any excess of these by liberal dressings of potash (woodashes and flyash are good sources) during early fall; or by sowing buckwheat in July or rye in September, or both these together in July. As these crops grow, they remove excess water and nitrogenous plant food from the soil and develop plants which, when plowed or

dug into the ground in spring, return the plant food and their own bodies to form humus.

Fortunately you can predict accurately enough for practical purposes when to expect frost. The daily forecasts by the weather bureau give suggestions as to the general weather to expect, but you can make your own observations and predictions. Local conditions influence temperature. For instance, a nearby body of water, such as a lake, the sea, a wide or a deep river, or even a large pond affects the rate at which air temperature changes. In spring, because the water is cold, it keeps the air also cold and thus more or less retards plant development. In autumn the reverse effect occurs; the water, being warm, not only warms the air, but fills it with water vapour, thus warding off frost.

Open and flat country and small villages are more likely to suffer from late spring and early autumn frosts than are large cities and their nearby suburbs because, in the former, heat loss by radiation into space is more rapid in clear, clean air and under cloudless skies than in the latter, where the air is filled with smoke and dust and where the fires in countless houses, factories, and other buildings directly raise the temperature.

Dark-coloured, sandy, and well-drained soils absorb and hold more sun heat than do light-coloured, clayey, and poorly-drained ones, so are less likely to be frosty. Other conditions being equal, southern and eastern slopes are also warmer than western ones, because they more quickly absorb the sun's rays. Though this favours earliness of plant development, it often makes the growing of certain fruits (apricot, peach, Japanese plum) precarious or impossible, because the flowers are encouraged to open so early that spring frost kills them and thus prevents fruit production, though not usually killing the trees.

You can discover for yourselves that cold air, being heavier than warm air, flows like water from high to low ground and "settles" in hollows or "pockets" unless it can drain to still lower levels or be driven out by wind; that frosts are much more likely to occur when the air is still, the sky clear, and the stars brilliant, than when there is wind or clouds, especially when the former is strong and the latter cover the whole sky. The direction and force of the wind also help in making a local forecast. One that blows strongly from the north is far more likely to bring cool or cold weather than one from the south, just as one from the east is likely to bring clouds and rain, and one from the west clear skies and colder weather. The rate at which the barometer rises also helps, because it indicates the approach of clear weather and, if rapid, also of cold weather.

An unusually warm spell is almost sure to be followed by a cooler or cold one, because the general weather moves in prodigious waves from southwest to northeast across the country. Hence a light frost following a warm spell is likely to do more damage than an even more severe one following cool weather. For this reason, you should be on your guard when one of these warm spells occurs in spring: be ready to protect your seedlings, newly transplanted plants, and the flowers on your fruit trees and bushes.

When the sky is cloudy, when there is fog, or even when a haze occurs during or toward evening, frost is less likely to occur than when the night is clear, because these conditions of moisture in the air prevent loss of heat from the earth.

A reliable sign of approaching frost is the rate at which the temperature falls during the late afternoon and early evening. Starting with 50°F. or less, clear skies, and no wind, a fall of 2°F. or more an hour between four and eight o'clock usually indicates that freezing temperatures will be reached before morning, unless clouds or winds develop or unless you do something to prevent frost.

In a small way, individual plants may be protected by inverted flower pots, peach baskets, and other receptacles placed over them, by newspapers spread and held in place by stones or clods of earth. A more convenient adaptation of this way is to use a light screen of burlap, mounted on a frame, placed over the plants or beds. These all tend to hold the heat around the plants.

Smouldering fires, which produce abundant smoke and steam, form artificial clouds which check radiation in the same way as do true clouds. When the air is still, the smoke spreads out evenly and proves effective as a protection nearly as far as the clouds extend. This method is not feasible where the smoke would prove objectionable to neighbours. Numerous small, bright fires of wood, coal, or (preferably) oil are used extensively by commercial growers of fruit and vegetables to heat the air. They are less useful in small areas than the methods already presented and those that follow.

The most generally feasible method is to fill the air with water vapour in one of the following ways: stirring the soil with the wheelhoe or the cultivator toward evening, to expose an increased surface of damp earth; sprinkling the plants, the ground, and the adjacent area with a hose nozzle that breaks up the water into small drops, or using an overhead irrigation system for this

purpose. The water evaporates and, as the vapour condenses, it liberates latent heat and thus checks the cooling process.

Freezing of the ground may injure even established trees, shrubs, and vines of some kind, so anything that will reduce the depth of frost penetration or prevent alternate freezing and thawing will tend to prevent such injury.

Experiment has proved that under sod, freezing reached a depth of 8 inches, whereas in an adjacent sodless area it reached 18 inches. Peach trees on the sod ground made healthy, uniform growth, whereas in the sodless soil they were slow to start, had many dead branches, and made poor development.

In another experiment, just before winter a few forkfuls of manure or shovelfuls of soil or peat were banked around the trunks of exceptionally vigorous peach trees, with the result that every tree so treated came through the winter without injury, whereas a few not banked all died.

When water freezes, it swells and lifts the crust of frozen earth above the unfrozen ground below. As it does so in autumn and early winter, it also lifts shallow rooted plants, roots and all. When it thaws, the soil settles back, but the plants do not. They are left with exposed roots. Each succeeding freeze lifts them some more and each thaw leaves them farther out of the ground, with the result that they dry and die. Hence the importance of applying a mulch in the fall.

In the spring equally fatal results may affect unmulched plants. When the surface thaws above a lower layer of still frozen earth, the thawed layer settles; and when it later freezes and lifts, it breaks the roots of small plants by pulling them. Hence, again, the importance of mulch; for beneath a sufficient layer of such loose material, heaving and settling are reduced to minimum and thawing of the ground proceeds from below upward, until the mulched soil has thawed out and thus eliminated danger of root breakage.

In order to have extra early beans, corn, melons, and cucumbers, I have often sown seed much earlier than was locally popular, thus risking frost damage. When no frost occured, I was ahead of competitors; and when it did come, I usually saved the plants by one of these methods. I have never thus risked transplanting eggplants, tomato, or pepper plants, because, even though not frozen, they "sulk" if chilled and start fruiting late.

In case you have not protected your plants and a frost has occurred during the night, you may be able to save them, even those covered with frost or whose tissues have been ruptured by freezing of their sap. Spray them with cold water as soon as possible after dawn or before sunrise and also shield them from direct sunlight after the sun appears, until they have thawed out and apparently resumed normal activity. Better keep them so shielded until between ten o'clock and noon. The most conveniently applied shield is the screen mounted on a frame with short legs.

Planting by the Signs & Phases of the Moon

by Dave Dawson

Gardening according to the phases and the zodiacal positions of the moon goes back to very ancient times. During the early stages of recorded history, mankind was very aware of the apparent passage of the sun, moon, planets, and stars around the earth, and held the phenomena of the celestial spheres in great awe and respect. Due to the tremendous magnitude of the heavens, and the stately order of their predictable patterned movement across the sky, early man probably formed many superstitions regarding their origin and purpose. But early historic man was also extremely aware of and in tune with his environment through sheer necessity of survival. Soon he began to notice a correlation between certain types of phenomena and the positions of the planets in the heavens. He noticed that people born at any given time of the year had certain general character traits held in common, for the most part, only with other people born around that time of year. He noticed that most maritime disasters happened during certain planetary configurations. But where this early man was most aware of the planetary influences was in the area most important to his continued preservation and well-being, which was the cultivation of plants to feed himself and his animals. Driven by a vital necessity for better crops, he became keenly aware of the moon's effect on the lives of the plants he cultivated. He also noticed that its effect was two-fold, as it affected growth according to its position in the Zodiac, and also according to its phases (from full moon to new and back to full). Through the centuries, man continued to plant according to the moon's position and phases, constantly adding to his knowledge of its effects on plant growth. Even today, a very large number of the world's farmers still plant according to the moon.

Although the idea of the moon having an effect on the growth and development of life on the earth has been under attack for several centuries now, it is just being learned through scientific research that the moon definitely does affect most living things on earth. Psychologists have discovered that the phases of the moon have a definite effect on the behaviour patterns of human beings. Scientists have discovered that clams do not open and close their shells according to the tide, as previously believed, but directly feel the position of the moon in the sky, although they are deep beneath the sea.

It is well known that the tides are controlled by the position of the moon in the sky, but what is not so well known is that as the moon grows from new to full, the tides get higher and the water table in the earth rises, while the opposite occurs when the moon progresses from full to new. Therefore, at the full moon, the ground would be expanded with moisture. If you were to sink a post into the ground, it would become quite loose as the moon waned, since the earth around it would contract with the loss of moisture. If you plant something which grows above ground, on the increase of the moon, the plant will find it increasingly easy to rush those vital liquids up the stem during the crucial early stages of growth, while if you plant it at the decrease of the moon, it will become increasingly more difficult, resulting in a stunted plant. Although through good fertilization, irrigation, and careful tending, much of the need to closely follow the moon is offset, it is still a useful aid to gardening; if you do all that and also plant by the moon you are that much more assured of a good crop.

First, I would like to outline a simple guide to enable you to figure out where the moon is at any given time, and then I shall give you the run-down on the best conditions for planting each crop.

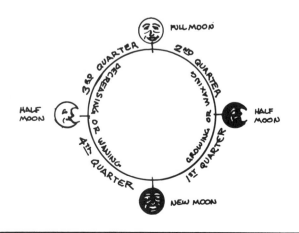

As you can see from the previous diagram, when the moon is growing from new to a half-moon, it is the first quarter; as it progresses from a half to a full moon, it is the second quarter; as it wanes from full to half, it is in the third quarter; and as it moves from half to new, it is in the fourth quarter.

If you know which sign and which degree of that sign the sun is in (in the Zodiac), you can also find the approximate zodiacal position of the moon by observing its phases. When the moon is new, it is in the same zodiacal position as the sun; when it is full, it is in the opposite sign, but the same degree. If it is a quarter moon waxing, then it is 45 degrees in advance of the sun; and if it is a quarter moon waning, it is 45 degrees behind the sun. Below is a diagrammatic example of this situation. Also given is the approximate time of year the sun enters each sign.

Each sign of the Zodiac contains 30 degrees, and as you can see from the diagram below, the sun is in each sign for about 30 days; therefore, you can approximately equate each day of the sun's progression into a sign with one degree of progression. The sun moves counter-clockwise around the Zodiac. When the moon is half full and growing, it is 90 degrees in advance of the sun; when it is half full but waning, it is 90 degrees behind the sun; when it is full, it is 180 degrees from, or opposite the sun; and when it is new, it is 0 degrees or in the same position as the sun.

Planting by the Phases of the Moon

Generally all crops which produce avove the ground and mature in one growing season should be planted during the increase of the moon. All crops which produce below the ground and crops which take more than one year to produce should be planted at the decrease or waning of the moon.

More specifically you should plant leafy plants of one-season duration such as lettuce, cabbage, brussel sprouts, cauliflower, broccoli, asparagus, spinach, etc. during the first quarter. Also grains do well, if planted in the first quarter. All these may be planted in the second quarter, if you are unable to plant them during the first.

All-in-one-season plants, which contain their seed within the fruit of the plant and grow on vines, should be planted in the second quarter. Examples are melons, pumpkins, squash, tomatoes, beans, and peas. All these may be planted during the first quarter, if you are unable to plant them during the second. Grains may also be planted during the second quarter.

During the third quarter, plant all crops which take more than one growing season to mature, including all trees, shrubs, berries, winter wheat; also all bulb and root crops such as onions, potatoes, turnips, radishes, parsnips, carrots, onions, and rhubarb.

The fourth quarter can be used for the same crops as the third quarter, but it is best for killing pests, pulling weeds, and preparing the soil.

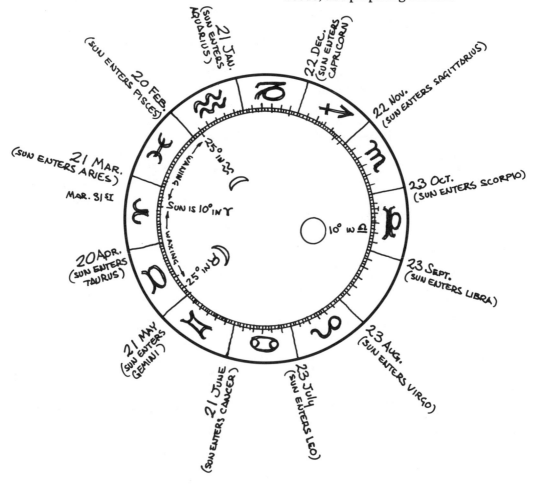

Planting According to the Sign of the Moon

Moon in Aries — this is a barren, dry sign and is good for killing weeds and pests. It is not good for planting, but it is good for cultivation.

Moon in Taurus — this sign is moist and productive. It is an earthly sign and is very good for root crops, and also good for leafy vegetables. Makes plants hardy.

Moon in Gemini — this sign is barren and dry. Good for destroying weeds and pests, but not good for planting. Cultivate,

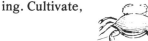

Moon in Cancer — this sign is moist and is the most fruitful of all signs. It is the best sign for planting all crops, especially above ground; also good for irrigation.

Moon in Leo — this is the most barren and dry of all the signs of the Zodiac. It is the worst sign for planting, but is the best for destroying weeds and pests. Good for cultivation.

Moon in Virgo — this sign, although moist and earthy, is barren and is not good for planting. Good for destroying weeds and cultivation.

Moon in Libra — this sign is somewhat moist and semi-fruitful. Very good for flowers, if beauty is desired. Good for the growth of roots and the pulp of the plant.

Moon in Scorpio — a very fruitful and moist sign. Good for all crops. Very good for vines.

Moon in Sagittarius — barren and dry. Good for cultivation.

Moon in Capricorn—fruitful, somewhat moist, and earthy. Good for root crops.

Moon in Aquarius—This is a dry barren sign and is good for destroying weeds, pests and for cultivation.

Moon in Pisces — very fruitful and moist. This sign is the second best for all crops, especially for root crops. Good for irrigation.

For the best results, you should try to get a situation where the moon is in the best quarter and best sign simultaneously. This is not always possible, of course, and you should not hesitate to use one of the secondary signs or quarters. Remember also that you should not depend too heavily on the moon, for there are many other important factors in proper gardening, such as getting the crop in as soon after the last frost as possible (especially here in the northern latitudes, where the growing season is so short), good fertile soil, irrigation, and loving care. All these factors combine in order to bring you a healthy crop with a high yield.

Other Useful Hints

Harvest crops when the moon is waning or decreasing; this is especially important for fruits, as they tend to spoil easily otherwise; also when the moon is a dry sign. Cut timber when the moon is waning, to prevent rot and worm infestation. Set posts in the ground when the moon is waning, to prevent loosening. Harvest root crops for seed at or shortly after the full moon.

Irrigate when the moon is in a watery sign. Can vegetables, jelly, preserves, and pickles when the moon is in Sagittarius or Gemini and also in the fourth quarter.

Prune during the third quarter and when the moon is in Scorpio. Graft just before the sap begins to flow, when the moon is in the first or second quarter and in a watery sign.

For hatching eggs, Cancer or Pisces will be best for quck maturation and good layers.

For a complete and easy to follow guide to planting by the moon, with the position of the moon by sign and quarter for every day of the year given, I recommend you get *Llewellyn's Moon Sign Book and Daily Planetay Guide;* if you cannot find it in a book store, order it direct from:
Llewellyn Publications
Box 3383 - MSB
St. Paul, Minn. 55165
USA

Gravity Feed Water Supply

by Hugh Eliot

How Much Water?

After access to a homesite, a water supply is next in importance. Electric power and telephone are relative luxuries. Just as we assume access by means of a motor vehicle, in these days a water supply means a piped supply. In B.C. in particular there is often a supply of good water at a higher level than a house site. To help those who want to install their own gravity supply, I will try to deal with some of the problems involved and state in a simple way the laws of hydraulics involved. I assume the problem is to obtain water from a stream and that plastic pipe will be used.

How much of a supply do you need? To run a sprinkler with a 30-ft. radius and still be able to fill a bath without interfering with either operation — 10 gallons per minute at 20 pounds per square in. (p.s.i.). Is it available? What size pipe should be used? How deeply should it be buried?

The Survey

To get any answer to these problems, you have to find out the distance from the source to the site and what the difference in level or head is. First, go over the route. Determine its direction and mark it out with stakes. Where it goes through bush, slash a line of sight. To measure the distance, use a steel tape or a piece of wire 200 to 300 ft. long. Put in pegs each time the wire is moved along a length, marking the pegs with the distance.

On a preliminary survey, the relative heights of the source and the site might be taken off a map, if a large one is available. The best map is one which is scaled one-half in. to the mile with 50 ft. contours. It will help to check with your own survey. This can be done with an 18-in. carpenter's level and a 15 to 20 ft. pole. The pole should be marked at 1 ft. increments, as well as a high-lighted marker every 5 ft. The process involves setting up the level on a box or table. Make it level and then sight along to the pole at a 100, 200, or 300 ft. distance. The person holding the pole can help by pointing to the bars with another stick, clearly identifying the bar sighted. The level can then be set up at the foot of the pole and the pole moved farther down the slope. The process can be used to find the relative level of the site below the source, adding all the steps together. In the preliminary survey, it will be sufficient to determine the gradient in per cent of each stretch of the route where it is seen to change. Multiply the distance on the ground by this percentage and then add up these drops. Check them against altitudes on a map. For example, if the level is 2-1/2 ft. off the ground and sights to the 14-ft. bar, the difference in level between the two points is minus 2-1/2, or 11-1/2 ft. If the distance between the level and the pole is 120 ft., the gradient is 11.5/120 x 100, or 9 per cent. With care, this kind of survey could yield all the data necessary to know if the system would work and what it would cost. The length of the route is the sum of the sections. The drop or head available is the drops in each section. The average total gradient as a per cent is the total drop over the total distance times 100.

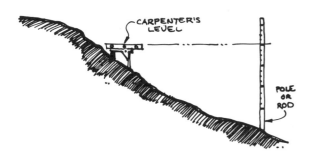

Necessary Pressure

What will the pressure be at the house? What should it be? It should be at least 20 p.s.i. to come out of domestic fittings, so that you don't have to wait a minute to fill a kettle and half an hour to get a bath. Each pound per sq. in. is the result of 2.6 ft. of head or drop in the supply line. To produce 20 p.s.i., you will need 52 ft. of head *but* that will only be the static head. As soon as you turn a tap on and start drawing water, the pressure drops. How much? It depends on the size of the pipe and rate of flow. It is stated in tables as the loss of head in ft. per 100 ft. of lengths of pipe for different rates of flow. A table (available from the manufacturers of plastic pipe) would show that for a flow of 10 gallons per minute, there is a loss of 2 ft. of head or .8 of p.s.i. If the drop in your line is only 5 ft. per 100 ft. of run, 40 per cent of your pressure will be lost in friction. If your line is coming down a mountain on a 25 per cent gradient, the loss will be only 2 ft. in 25 ft., or 8 per cent of the head.

Choosing Your Pipe

It's said lightly that the way to choose the size of pipe is to decide on the largest pipe you can afford, borrow some more money, and get the next largest size — then you'll have the proper pipe. Pipe cannot be too big, except for its cost; and the fact that, for a given wall thickness, as a pipe gets larger, the pressure it will withstand gets smaller. As a rule of thumb figure for a preliminary survey, I would suggest that for a line to a single homestead with some garden and a lawn, if the overall gradient of the line is around 5 per cent, the pipe should be 1-½ in. inside diameter; around 10 per cent gradient, 1-¼ in. i.d.; over 20 per cent gradient, 1 in. pipe, if it will withstand the pressure involved.

There can be two regrets after laying a water line, both quite futile — the pipe is not large enough and, in the colder climates, the pipe is not buried deeply enough for winter temperatures. Skimp on burying a pipe, and you'd better build an out-house. Nothing goes out of commission quicker than indoor plumbing when the water freezes. Listen to the more conservative estimates of necessary depth. Relative savings can be made where a pipe is in bush; but where pipe is under a road or footpath, or wherever snow might be removed or packed, bury it the maximum depth for the area. Keeping water running to prevent a line from freezing is not very practical. Too many accidents may happen. It's also wasteful and illegal to use water this way.

Other common practical problems are: (a) assuring enough water over the end of the pipe at the intake to fill it at all levels of the creek; (b) getting rid of dirt in the water. The theory of getting rid of dirt is very simple — much theory is. Fast-moving water can carry dirt. Standing water will drop it. So water should stand nearly still for a time, before entering the pipe. That means storing a hundred gallons in a tank, pool, or ditch with a very slight drop. Whatever the arrangement is, it must not freeze, and there must be some arrangement for flushing out the material that has settled out. None of these things are easy to arrange when obtaining water from a creek at the bottom of a narrow, steep ravine. That is the kind of a creek that will be heavy with silt when it's in flood. The common approach to such a creek is a trail, sloping uphill very slightly, bulldozed into the hillside. Bulldozing is expensive; $10 to $15 per hour. Sometimes this much of a capital cost can be shared, as well as parts of pipe trenches to different homes. That begs the question why not a communal water supply — which gets into social, legal, and economic engineering. The behaviour of people over water is a far more complicated business than the behaviour of water itself.

Air in a pipe obstructs flow of water. There should be valves all along the line to release air, especially if the route is a series of humps and dips. It is best that a route should slope uniformly downhill, but where the terrain is irregular, the line will work if there is an air bleeder at the bottom of each dip or at least at every splice between 300 ft. lengths of pipe. A bleeder in its simplest from is a

STAKES 2'-0" HIGHER THAN DEEPEST SNOW EXPECTED

VALVES IN HOLES DUG BELOW FROST LINE

DAM

INTAKE FILTER

5'-0"

T instead of a sleeve joining two lengths of pipe and a hose valve on the branch line; this is installed in a frost-proof hand hole and marked with a stake higher than the deepest snow expected.

Another simple but important point: where a pipe leaves a creek along an almost level trail cut in the hillside, try to arrange that there are a few feet of head immediately after the water enters the pipe. Locate your intake works 5 ft. vertically or 50 ft. of pipe on a 10 per cent grade from the beginning of the level stretch. Put a bleeder there and at the next splice down the level stretch.

Remember that your bleeder points are test points. When there is trouble with frost, dirt, or air, you may be able to recover your shortcomings as a hydraulic engineer with the bleeders. Put durable markers to show the location of the pipe and/or splices. It may be years before you or someone else wants to know where it is. I suggest that you bury a number of one gallon cans of concrete flush with the ground. Inscribe in the wet cement pertinent information about the pipe.

2" pipe splice 12' 8'-0" deep

Some considerations *before* spending money on a water supply:

(1) See the government department concerned with water. How much will they allow you to take from the creek? What are the requirements to obtain a licence? In my experience, Water Rights engineers are very helpful even beyond information about official requirements.

(2) Find out the history of the creek from old inhabitants. Does it ever dry up? Does it flood badly?

(3) Is the creek water fit for drinking? Is it likely to become polluted? Is there building land for sale upstream?

(4) Laying a pipe line: legal, personal, engineering, financial. What are your rights? Are your neighbours agreeable? Are they interested in sharing the cost of a

ditch and intake works? My experience is that people are able to share these items. but not the pipe itself. Everyone lays their own pipe. As the neighbourhood develops and the land gets sub-divided, it becomes a plastic spider web — one reason for putting in precise durable markers showing where *your* pipe is.

(5) Digging the ditch: Get estimates from the back-hoe operators and consider with them the possibilities of hitting rock, other pipes, and buried cables. Get permission and the requirements for crossing a public highway. It generally requires an outer steel pipe to be buried at a depth specified by the highway department.

Chuck Valentine, a neighbour of Hugh Eliot, has also hassled with homestead water problems. Here he comments upon Hugh's article and relates a few of his own experiences.

v. m.

I feel 20 p.s.i. static pressure is minimal. Try for 60 to 80 pounds if you can. Once you start gardening a homestead, demands for water will grow from year to year and a dry spell brings all the demands at once. Every valve you turn on drops the pressure, due to friction losses in the pipe. Modern faucets are designed for higher city pressures and let little water through.

While Hugh's survey will work well, I find it cumbersome. It almost takes two people to sight a carpenter's level in the bush, and someone must carry the rod too. A method I always use is quite accurate enough for a home water supply:

Buy a small, cheap hand level. Measure the height of your own eye while standing erect on the ground. Start at your house-site and follow any route that will take you to your intended intake point at the stream. You don't have to follow the route of your pipe, which may be inaccessible at this planning stage. Sight horizontally through the level to any object on the ground that you can identify and sight on: a rock, stick, tuft of grass, child's hand, or foot. Then walk and stand there and sight again. Each sighting will take you one eye-height higher. When you reach your intake point, multiply number of sightings by eye height and voila! you will have the height of your intake above your house. Then lend the hand level to anyone else who needs it. My $4.00 hand level has been used for 18 years in our community this way. These levels have a bubble, a little mirror set at 45 degrees to see the bubble, a small peep hole, and a cross hair. To use them, just line up the bubble and the cross-hair (which appear side by side) and see what you're looking at. Certainly accurate within 5 per cent, probably better. Also good for levelling post and beam buildings, irrigation ditches, and drainage ditches.

The figure for head or drop to produce each pound per square inch pressure is 2.31 ft.

Hugh's figures (at the end of paragraph "Necessary Pressure"), as he says, are dependent on size of pipe, but he doesn't say what size pipe he refers to. Take them as a general idea of losses to be encountered, not to calculate from.

Without specifically checking his figures I agree from practice here that 1-1/4-in. and 1-1/2-in. plastic pipes are suitable sizes for 10 per cent and 5 per cent graients. Never go smaller than 1-in. for most purposes, and even that is questionable.

Don't miss that important point about arranging some drop in the pipe first, if you have to go near-horizontally out of the creek canyon. It's very hard to start water through a near-horizontal pipe. Regarding bleeder valves along the pipe route, I've never seen this done, but would think they should be at the high points if they are to let air out, not at low points. Air rises and it's hard to get it out of the low points.

Do check the pressure range of your pipe before you buy it. If you have to have high pressure, over 80 pounds, buy heavier strength pipe for that portion of the line, not a smaller size. Avoid having the larger sizes of plastic pipe (1-in. and over) lying on the ground in the hot sun with water pressure in them and no water flowing. Then they can heat up, weaken, expand, and perhaps burst.

By the way, don't take that lightly about borrowing money to buy the next larger pipe than you can afford. I wish I had followed that advice myself.

When burying plastic pipe, cover it first with fine material, and be careful not to have large rocks over it: they could collapse it later. Best also to fill the pipe with water before backfilling, for strength and pre-shrinking.

Intake Filters

My intake is quite makeshift, but seldom requires a trip to the creek. I formed a 5-in. cylinder about 16-in. long out of a piece of very heavy brass screening I found on this place. I bolted one end to an extremely heavy brass casting I found (using brass bolts) and plugged the other end with a circle of cedar board, nailed on. The casting, probably a packing gland for an inboard propeller shaft, had a hole the right size to take a plastic pipe fitting! Then I wrapped the whole thing with a brass mosquito-size screening, clamped on with stainless-steel clamps meant for 5-in. plastic pipe. I simply dropped the heavy thing to the creek bottom and kept it from washing downstream by driving a piece of drill steel into the creek bed.

Some sand and sediment leaked through this and it was always a nuisance, so for the main house I ran the entire supply through an old hot-water tank (or "range boiler," the type that connects to a waterfront on a wood-coal stove) 12-in. in diameter and 60-in. high. Plugging the side holes, I cut off the filler pipe, so that it extends only half-way down the inside of the tank from the top. This throws the dirt to the bottom of the tank at rather high speed, but the water rises slowly through the 12-in. tank to the outlet at the top, leaving the sediment behind. Works quite well. Needs cleaning about twice a year.

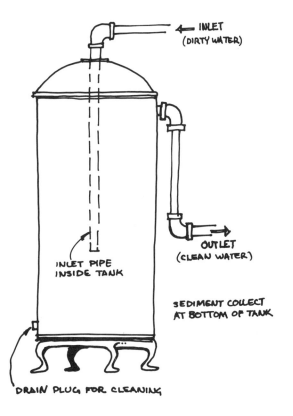

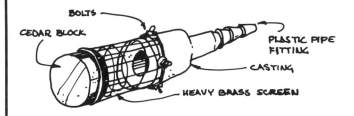

Beehive Defense

by Eric Anderson

My main purpose in writing this article is not so much to gather and list in one place the natural predators of the honey bee and preventative measures, but to focus attention on a problem. When it comes to protecting the hive from ants and moths, there are plenty of poisons that work very well. Too well sometimes. If you have problems with mice, there are poisons for them as well. A couple of grains of strychnine on an egg will stop the skunks, and all the raccoons, weasels, coyotes, and other animals that happen to like eggs. Then there is the bear. He's a little bigger problem, but with a little patience, lots of ammunition, and a 30.06, he won't cause any trouble. When I was doing my research for this article, I came up with nearly the same solution everytime: traps, guns, and poisons. After seeing my own hives destroyed by a black bear, not once, but twice in one week, I have sympathy with persons who still stick with those guaranteed but destructive methods. What else is there that really works? I don't have a lot of new and useful information, but I hope this will represent a core to work from, a core to test experiment with and improve upon.

A little care in storing combs will prevent a lot of trouble at a later date. The best storage area is a building that is dry, ventilated, well lighted, and bee or mouse-proof. The first condition is essential. Most sheds, especially the older ones, seem to be naturally well ventilated. The last two conditions: well, sometime you'll get around to building a new shed, but until them there are a few things you can do.

First of all, before storing the empty supers away, put them back on the hive for a week or two. This will give the bees a chance to clean them up for you and greatly reduce the attraction to any pest. When storing the supers, they should be in piles five or six high, with a queen excluder on the top and bottom to keep out any rodents. Between each super, lay a couple of sheets of newspaper; the ink will act as a repellent to the wax moth and seals the ants out. Water will keep ants away. A friend of mine, while doing her extracting, found that ants entered her porch by the space under the door. She kept a water sprinkler running there day and night until she was finished. If the supers are elevated on a stand or table, and the legs put in cans of oil, you can cut off the ants' access routes. This is probably the best solution, allowing you to forget the newspaper which blocks out light and ventilation, two conditions which are essential when dealing with the wax moth. In the north, the wax moth can't survive the cold temperatures (45° F. and below), so insulating the storage area is not necessary. When temperatures rise above 60° F., check for signs of tunnelling and boring, as well as webs and debris. To destroy these pests once the frames have been infected, you can heat the equipment at a temperature of 116° to 120°F. for 80 minutes.

Out in the yard, the hive can suffer damage from bears, skunks, ground hogs, woodchucks, and wasps, as well as from ants, wax moths, and mice. The important thing about these latter three is that they cannot do much damage unless the colony is weak, diseased, or starved. Other than keeping the hive dry by checking and placing the supers directly in line with the previous ones, there is not much that can be done to safeguard against the wax moth.

Ants attack the bees and the stores. Very often they are found between the top and the inner cover. By removing the inner cover for a week, the ants will be limited in their attack to the front entrance, which the bees are capable of defending. You can put the legs of the stand in cans and then put the can-covered legs in larger cans filled with oil. By keeping vegetation around the hive to a minimum and spreading small amounts of ash on the ground, you will further restrict the ants' access to the hive.

Mice enter the hive during the winter and build nests in the comb. The cluster supplies them with warmth. They will eat the bees and stores, leaving the hive occasionally for water. Besides destroying the comb, they urinate on the bees and constantly irritate

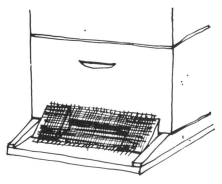

them, often causing the cluster to break up in cold weather. Signs of their presence are bits of chewed wax or feces at the hive entrance, and a heavy odour when the hive top is lifted. In winter when the flights of bees are few, a wire screen (1/4'' to 3/8'' mesh) on triangular blocks is placed across the entrance way.

The skunk attacks the hive at night. He scratches at the entrance of the hive and, as the bees come out to investigate, he gobbles them up. As more bees come out, he is forced to squash them and at the same time roll them into a ball, which he then eats. The beekeeper can always be sure when this pest is present by the scratches and mud on the front of the hive. Also there will be a small area that is polished smooth — the vegetation worn away from the mashing and rolling action. To prevent the skunk from using this area and thus defeat his attack, a screen with one-inch mesh should be securely placed three or four inches off the ground and level with the entrance. Another method of defence is to put a wire mesh fence around the hive. To discourage the skunk from digging underneath the fence, the wire mesh should be extended at least two feet out from the base and buried.

Bears, mainly because of their size, are probably the most difficult problem to overcome. Their power enables them to smash and completely destroy a hive in one raid. They don't often have trouble getting past defence structures. Once they have had the taste of honey (the adults actually prefer the brood), you can be sure they will return until the last is gone. It seems the answer is to convince the bear that he shouldn't bother, and that whatever is there he won't like. If you are lucky, you can quite often pull it off, but there is always one bear that is a little more persistent than the others. As one beekeeper told me: "Every bear is different and their method of attack is often unique." They have been known to lift up a hive, carry it off a considerable distance, put it down, calmly start batting supers off in all directions. With the hive seriously divided into groups around the original location and the scattered supers, the bear has easy pickings. He pulls out a few frames and heads off a short distance from all the confusion to eat his dinner in peace.

Until now, the main concept in bear protection has been to build a defence perimeter around the yard. This has been done with crosscut saws, boards with spikes in them, barb wire — just about anything you can think of. The most sophisticated and successful method is the electric fence. They can be purchased through farmer and dairy co-ops for about $25. To make the electrical ground more effective, two feet of No. 16 chicken wire should be laid flat around the outside of the fenced-off area and connected to the controller output.

½" MESH SCREEN ON WIRE FRAME

SCREEN BURIED MIN. 8"

2'-0" MIN.

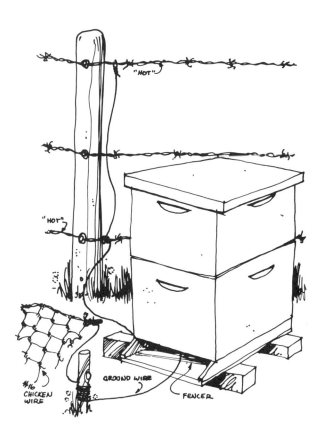

"HOT"

"HOT"

#16 CHICKEN WIRE

GROUND WIRE

FENCER

Strips of bacon can be placed on the barb wire to guarantee a surprising shock. Considering the price of the unit, it's a good idea to house it in an empty hive just inside the fence. The only problem with the electric fence is that it is not completely bear proof. Understandably there are laws that limit the voltage, so the main element becomes surprise. If for some reason things haven't gone well for the bear that day, it is possible he will feel an urge to destroy the thing that bothers him. With a couple of blows, he can easily knock the fence down.

The raised platform is also quite common, especially with the keeper who has only a few hives. Although severely limited in space and manoeuvreability, the stand can be very successful. The first requirement is soft ground, to allow you to securely place four 3'' pipes, 8' to 10' long, in a 4' square. Welded at the top of each pipe, you should have a plate (4'' x 4'') to bolt the wooden frame and platform to. It is possible to substitute trees for the pipe, which would give you the extra stability, but they must be covered well with very smooth tin. This is a mistake I made last year. I had covered the trees, but it was a patch job. I used many different pieces, some of it very bent and crumpled, so the surface wasn't smooth enough. The bear had no trouble climbing up and pushing a couple of hives over. Some people claim they can't climb at all, but are excellent pole vaulters. As I didn't see any marks on the tree that definitely proved he had climbed up, I can only suppose that he had little trouble holding on to the tin. Although quite exposed to the weather, the top of a shed also makes a very sturdy and unclimbable platform.

Another method which is more costly, but very handy if you move your bees out to the field in the spring and back to the wintering yard in the fall, is the caged trailer. The cage should be built with a wooden frame covered by heavy link fencing.

The trailer will eliminate time spent setting up fences and handling hives. Cost is the big drawback but often enough you can find heavy gauge link fencing second hand from old baseball diamonds, tennis courts, etc.

The newest concept in dealing with bears is to protect the target rather than the perimeter. The hives are placed back to back on top of a roll of 16-gauge (4'') netted wire. The wire is taken over the ends and top, then cinched tightly together. A second roll is wrapped around the sides and ends. It is also tightly cinched together. The hives are then covered with a light layer of mesh, the ends having a double layer. Along the top edges, the first wrap is connected to the second. This is repeated with a loose covering held down with four posts sunk into the ground and joined with straps. When the bees are attacked, they unite to fight the bear. There is no way that the bear can divide the colonies or the hive.

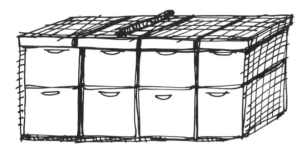

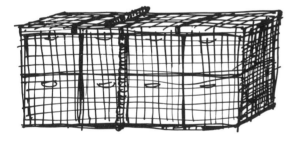

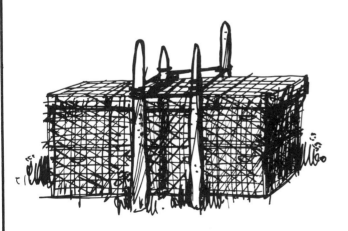

The major problem with this system concerns the temperament of the bees. If disturbed often by a persistent bear, the bees become angry and consume large amounts of the honey stores. The time-consuming problem of working with the wrappings is remedied with good spring management and extra supers early in the season. You shouldn't have to check the hives more than once or twice during the honey flow.

There are a few other pests that harm the hive or the bees in one way or another. Birds will catch bees in the field. Woodchucks chew on the supers, apparently looking for salt. They can be stopped with fences. Wasps will eat stray bees and often enter the hive to rob the stores. Dragonflies and robber flies will also prey on the bees away from the hive. Most of these pests are minor characters and their damage is insignificant.

If you are just beginning with bees, then give some special attention to location. Bears are attracted to orchards in late summer and fall. A blueberry crop will also bring them around. Ants thrive in pest areas. In Germany, wasps living in areas where a lot of ash had been dumped, forced beekeepers out of business. Remember, most of the larger animals are afraid of man, so the closer to the house and lights the better.

Bibliography

Beekeeping in the U.S.
Agricultural Handbook 335

Controlling the Greater Wax Moth
Farmers Bulletin 2217

Both are available from:
The Superintendent of Documents
U.S. Government Printing Office
Washington, D.C. 20402

Bee Diseases and Pest of the Apiary
Ontario Department of Agriculture
Parliament Buildings
Toronto, Ontario

A Treadle Driven Wood Turning Lathe

by W.C. Lecky

With the exception of turned wooden pulleys and the form to cast a flywheel, you can build this efficient treadle lathe with a few hand tools. Distance between centres can be increased to accommodate turnings more than 30 in. long, but in doing so, the treadle, which must be correspondingly lengthened, is apt to twist when pedaling is done at the tailstock end. Spindle height is such to enable one to pedal the lathe from either a standing or sitting position. Approximately 100 downward strokes of the treadle per minute will give a spindle speed recommended for turning. Common 2 by 4-in. fir stock is satisfactory for the stand. Side and front views in figure 8 give the correct length to cut each member. Note how the headstock is incorporated in the twin front legs. Except for fastening the bed pieces, the type of assembly shown to the right of figure 3 is used throughout, which permits tightening joints that may become loose. The small pin indicated is provided to keep the members in line when drawing up the bolts. Endless V-belting or round leather belting, joined, will do to rig the countershaft. As no tension adjustment is provided, it will be necessary, if an endless belt is used to drive the headstock spindle, to

vary the position of the rear countershaft pulley to be able to stretch the belt snugly over it. Belt dressing can be used if slipping develops.

Ball bearings in both the headstock and countershaft make the lathe exceptionally smooth running and are preferred to bronze bearings, although Ford model-T spindle body bushings can be used if you are unable to secure ball bearings. Figure 9 details the headstock. The holes for the bearings must be centered an equal distance above the bed and counterboard on facing sides to provide a press fit for the bearings. An auto-generator bearing will do for the inner bearing, but the outer one should be of the type to take end thrust when pressure is applied by the tailstock. The 3-in. pulleys, beside the drive and tail centres, are standard and come fitted with setscrews for attaching them to a 1/2-in. shaft. A 6 or 8-in. grinding wheel fitted to the outer end of the spindle serves a double purpose in providing a means for sharpening your lathe tools and at the same time contributing to the momentum. Collars are used against each bearing to take up end play.

The flywheel detailed in figures 5 and 6 provides the

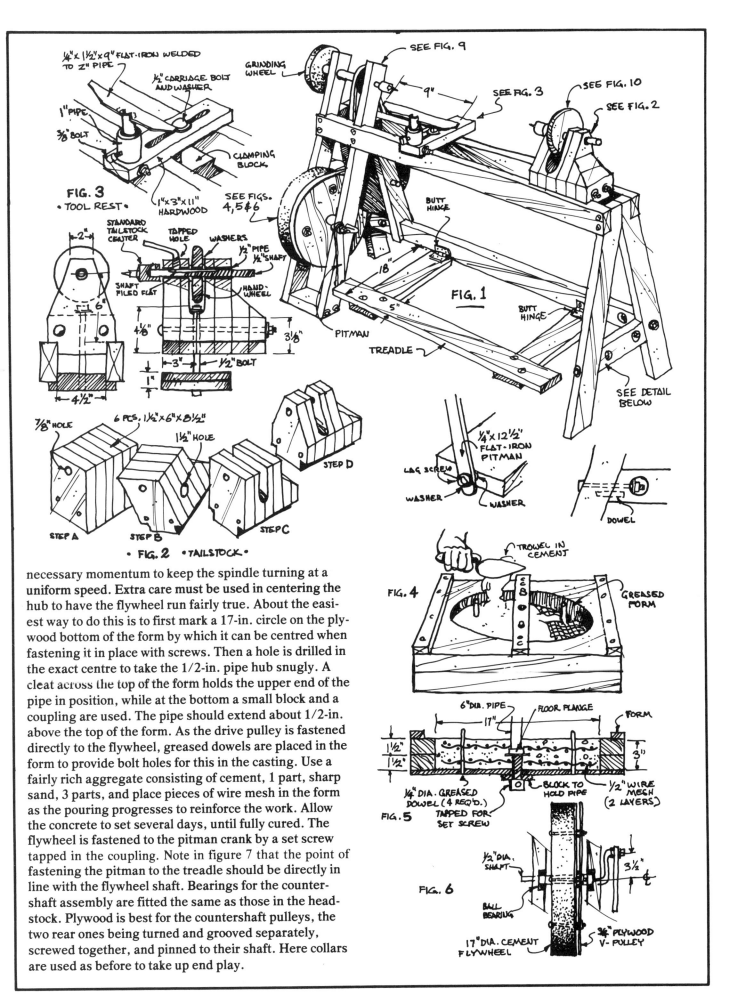

FIG. 3 • TOOL REST •

¼"x 1½"x 9" FLAT-IRON WELDED TO 2" PIPE

½" CARRIAGE BOLT AND WASHER

1" PIPE

3/8 BOLT

CLAMPING BLOCK

1"x3"x11" HARDWOOD

SEE FIGS. 4,5&6

SEE FIG. 9

GRINDING WHEEL

9"

SEE FIG. 3

SEE FIG. 10

SEE FIG. 2

BUTT HINGE

FIG. 1

18"

5"

BUTT HINGE

PITMAN

TREADLE

SEE DETAIL BELOW

STANDARD TAILSTOCK CENTER

TAPPED HOLE

WASHERS

½" PIPE

½" SHAFT

SHAFT FILED FLAT

HAND WHEEL

2"

6"

4⅛"

3⅛"

3"

½" BOLT

1"

4½"

7/8" HOLE

6 PCS. 1½"x6"x8½"

1½" HOLE

STEP D

STEP A

STEP B

STEP C

• FIG. 2 • TAILSTOCK •

¼"x 12½" FLAT-IRON PITMAN

LAG SCREW

WASHER

WASHER

DOWEL

FIG. 4

TROWEL IN CEMENT

GREASED FORM

6" DIA. PIPE

FLOOR FLANGE

FORM

17"

1½"

1½"

3"

¼" DIA. GREASED DOWEL (4 REQ'D.) TAPPED FOR SET SCREW

BLOCK TO HOLD PIPE

½" WIRE MESH (2 LAYERS)

FIG. 5

½" DIA. SHAFT

3½"

FIG. 6

BALL BEARING

17" DIA. CEMENT FLYWHEEL

¾" PLYWOOD V- PULLEY

necessary momentum to keep the spindle turning at a uniform speed. Extra care must be used in centering the hub to have the flywheel run fairly true. About the easiest way to do this is to first mark a 17-in. circle on the plywood bottom of the form by which it can be centred when fastening it in place with screws. Then a hole is drilled in the exact centre to take the 1/2-in. pipe hub snugly. A cleat across the top of the form holds the upper end of the pipe in position, while at the bottom a small block and a coupling are used. The pipe should extend about 1/2-in. above the top of the form. As the drive pulley is fastened directly to the flywheel, greased dowels are placed in the form to provide bolt holes for this in the casting. Use a fairly rich aggregate consisting of cement, 1 part, sharp sand, 3 parts, and place pieces of wire mesh in the form as the pouring progresses to reinforce the work. Allow the concrete to set several days, until fully cured. The flywheel is fastened to the pitman crank by a set screw tapped in the coupling. Note in figure 7 that the point of fastening the pitman to the treadle should be directly in line with the flywheel shaft. Bearings for the counter-shaft assembly are fitted the same as those in the head-stock. Plywood is best for the countershaft pulleys, the two rear ones being turned and grooved separately, screwed together, and pinned to their shaft. Here collars are used as before to take up end play.

Figure 2 details the tailstock and shows the progressive steps to follow in shaping the glued-up block. The spindle hole, which is bored while the block is still square, is bushed on each side of the handwheel opening with a 1/2-in. pipe nipple to receive a 1/2-in. threaded shaft. Note that one side of the shaft is filed flat for the end of the lock lever, which keeps the spindle from turning when being advanced or withdrawn by the handwheel. The latter is of wood and has a threaded bushing imbedded in its centre to fit the spindle. Washers centre it in the opening. Both tailstock and tool rest clamp in place by handwheels fitted below the bed, as shown in figures 7 and 8. The tool rest and holder are made according to figure 3. The post socket, which consists of a 1-in. pipe nipple inside a coupling, is anchored to the base by boring a hole in the latter to take the coupling snugly and then drilling crosswise through both for a 3-1/2-in. carriage bolt.

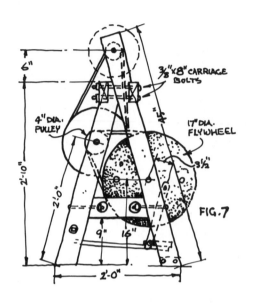

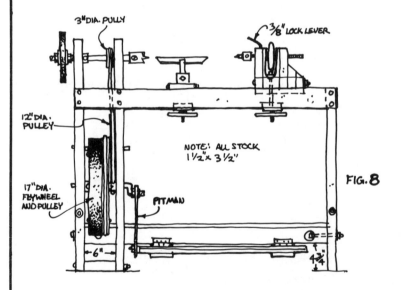

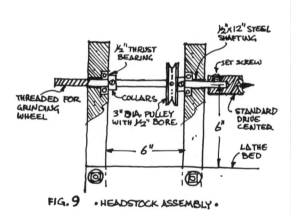

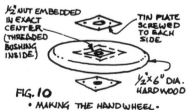

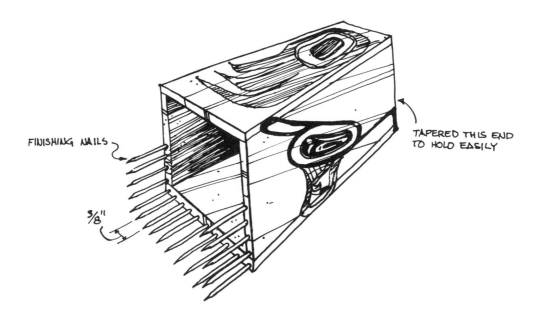

FINISHING NAILS

3/8"

TAPERED THIS END
TO HOLD EASILY

How to Build an Indian Berry Picker

Gathering the large, soft berries from blackberry, raspberry, thimbleberry, and salmonberry bushes presents no special problem except for the battle-of-the-thorn. But if you've ever spent the day popping huckleberries or any small berries from the bush, you must have wondered if there wasn't a better way of picking the small, round fruits. Well, folks, there is an answer, and it was the Indians who first came up with it. If you need lots of berries for those jellies, jams, and wines, have a large tribe to feed, or want to freeze or dry berries for winter use—and maybe sell some too—the Indian berry picker is the most efficient device to use. The original berry picker was usually whittled from wood in the shape of a scoop with a series of long V-shaped teeth at the mouth. The whittlers among us may want to carve their berry pickers Indian fashion. The rest of us can make our pickers from empty tin cans or nail together some lightweight wood to make the container.

If you use the tin can, solder pieces of steel or hard copper wire about 1/8" in diameter and 1-1/2" long in a semi-circle around the open end of the can. Space the wire (long finishing nails from the hardware store will also work) about 3/8" apart, and sharpen the ends of the wires to reasonably sharp points.

If you make your berry picker from wood, nail and glue together an open-ended box that you can hold comfortably in your hand. Tap long finishing nails into the end of the bottom and half-way up the sides, spacing the nails about 3/8" apart. Sharpen the nails with a file.

To use your Indian berry picker, simply run the points through the berry-laden plant limbs. The berries will fall into your picker along with a few leaves and twigs.

To separate the leaves from the berries, empty your day's collection of berries on a stretched and slanting blanket. The berries will roll and bounce to the bottom of the blanket to be caught in containers, and the few twigs and leaves will stay on the blanket and can be shaken away. Also you can separate the debris from the berries by placing everything in a pail of water. Any leaves that have been picked with the berries will float to the top and can be skimmed off.

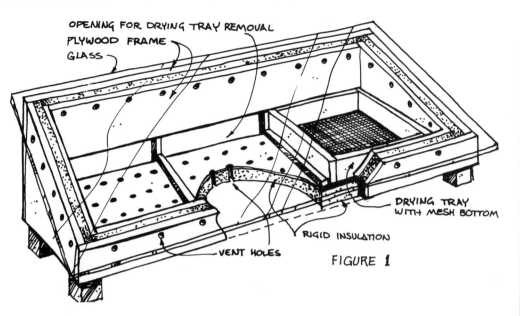

OPENING FOR DRYING TRAY REMOVAL
PLYWOOD FRAME
GLASS

DRYING TRAY
WITH MESH BOTTOM

RIGID INSULATION

VENT HOLES

FIGURE 1

A Solar Dryer

by T.A. Laward

The usual method of drying fruits is to lay them out in the sun for a few days until they seem to have dried out enough to be stored. It's cheap, but it does have its drawbacks; mainly bug and dust infestation. (Sun-dried apricots are nice, but I sure get tired of picking dust out from between my teeth.) To overcome the bugs and dust, as well as improve the quality of your produce (even reduction of the moisture to the low levels required makes a longer storage time possible), you might want to build a solar dryer.

Essentially, the dryer is a solar hot box. It consists of a rectangular container insulated at its base and preferably at the sides, and covered with a double-layered transparent roof. Solar radiation is transmitted through the roof and absorbed on the blackened interior surfaces. Owing to the insulation, the inside temperature is raised. Holes are drilled through the base to induce fresh ventilating air into the cabinet. Outlet ports are drilled on the upper parts of the cabinet side and rear panels. As the temperature increases, warm air passes out of the upper holes by natural convection, creating a partial vacuum and drawing fresh air up through the base. As a result there is a constant flow of air over your fruits (or vegetables), which are placed on perforated trays inside the cabinet.

Method of construction is limited only by your imagination, available materials, and a few general rules.

The length of the cabinet should be at least three times the width, so as to minimize the shading effect of the side panels.

Build the slope of the roof covering the angle designated in figure 2. This will give you the best angle for your latitude.

The transparent cover is best made of glass (1/8" or 3 mm.), although a polyester plastic film (about 0.005" thick) will also work.

You can build the framework out of most any building material. For the portable models, use wood, metal, hardboard, plywood, or even wicker or bamboo. If you wish to build something permanent, build it out of brick, stone, concrete, or maybe even adobe. When insulating,

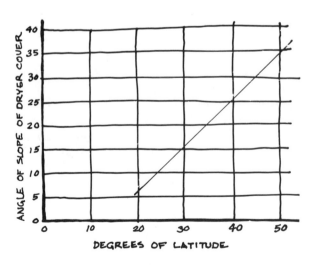

FIGURE 2

(y-axis) ANGLE OF SLOPE OF DRYER COVER
(x-axis) DEGREES OF LATITUDE

try to use cheap local materials such as wood shavings, sawdust, reject wool, or goat's hair.

Construct the hot box along lines similar to those outlined in figure 1. Make the insulation about 2'' thick, both for the base and the side sections. Drill holes in the insulated base and fit them with short lengths of plastic or rubberized garden hose. If there are bugs around, cover these insulation holes with fine mosquito netting or gauze. Usually, the high heat inside the cabinet discourages insects, rodents, etc. from entering and feeding on the drying produce.

Attach the transparent (glass or plastic) covers to a frame and fit the frame onto the chassis of the cabinet, making sure that the cover is completely watertight so as to avoid deterioration of the interior and wetting of the insulation. Paint the framework black in order to absorb the maximum solar radiation.

Now is the time to drill a couple of holes in the rear and side panels to provide ventilation ports to remove the warm, moist air. The number of holes is dependent on your climate and whatever it is you wish to dry. A good method is to initiate the drying in the springtime, with a minimum of side holes, and to continue drilling them so as just to prevent inside moisture condensation. This prevents drilling too many ventilation holes.

Fit the rear panel with access doors to give entry into the cabinet. Construct the trays of galvanized chicken-wire or some similar material. Place them on runners about 1/2'' high, so as to ensure a reasonable level of air circulation under and around the drying material.

Paint the inside of the cabinet black. The outside of the side, rear, and base panels should be painted with aluminum paint. If you wish to, cover the inside of the side and rear panels with a layer of aluminum foil (recycled of course) or if you have none, paint them black.

The dryer will handle about 1-1/2 pounds of produce per square foot of drying area. A small thermometer inserted into one of the ventilation holes will prove handy. Shield the thermometer bulb from direct sunlight. Temperature can be controlled by opening and closing the rear door, if necessary. Practice will allow you to determine the optimal termperatures.

Your produce should be perfect for drying. Use the blemished stuff for canning. Blemished or bruised fruits will not keep as well and may turn a whole tray of drying fruit bad. The smaller the pieces to be dried, the shorter the drying time. The layer of fruit should be no more than one piece deep.

Your fruit is dried when it feels dry on the outside, but slightly soft inside. It should not be brittle, nor should it be possible to squeeze out any juice. After the drying is finished, store the fruit in glass or cardboard containers. For four successive days, stir the contents thoroughly each day to bring the drier particles in contact with some that are more moist. If, at the end of 4 days, the fruit seems too moist, return it to the dryer for further treatment. Afterwards, store it in a cool place. It's a good idea to check it occasionally for molds.

FRUIT OR VEGETABLE	PREPARATION FOR DRYING AND DRYING METHOD
Beans (pod): String, Green, Snap, Wax	Wash and dry, cut or break off ends and pull strings, cut or break into one inch pieces, spread on frames or string on heavy thread, dry.
Beans (shelled): Lima, Pinto, Great Northern, Black, Soy, Kidney, Lentils, Pea (navy), Cranberry, Blackeyed peas, Cow-peas	Shell, grade if desired, spread on frames, stir daily until completely dry.
Peas: All types	Prepare and dry as for beans.
Cereal and bread grains: Barley, Corn, Oats, Rye, Buckwheat, Rice	Spread on frames, stir daily until completely dry. Allow corn to stand on the stalks until fully mature, pick and husk, leave on cobs until grains are hard, strip from cob.
Herbaceous plants	If the plants have thick, juicy stems such as celery or rhubarb, slice thinly and spread on frames or string on heavy thread. Dry all other herbs whole, crumble when dry and separate large stems from leaves, store in air-tight containers.
Peppers: Bell, Green, Red, Cherry, Banana, Tabasco	Small peppers (Tabasco, Red) may be dried whole. Slice others in rings and spread on frames or string on heavy thread.
Tuberous root vegetables: Beets, Carrots, Parsnips, Potatoes, Salsify, Sweet potatoes, Yams, Turnips, Rutabagas	Peel or scrape skins, slice thinly and spread on frames, or cube and string on heavy thread. NOTE: When these vegetables dry, they may change colour due to oxidation, but the colour change will in no way harm the flavour.
Bulbous root vegetables: Onions, Leeks, Kohlrabi	Peel and slice into thin rings (no more than $\frac{1}{8}$ inch thick), spread on frames or string on heavy thread.
Apples: All types	Wash, peel, slice into rings (no need to core), spread on frames or string on heavy thread. NOTE: Apples turn brown when dried due to oxidation, but the colour change does not affect the flavour.
Apricots: All types	Wash, cut in half and remove pit, spread skin side down on frames until dry. DO NOT TURN.
Berries: Blackberries, Blueberries, Loganberries, Gooseberries, Huckleberries, Raspberries, (black, red) Strawberries, Serviceberries, Mulberries, Juneberries, Shadberries, etc.	Wash, spread on frames until dry.
Cherries: All types	Wash, spread on frames until dry.
Currants: All types	Pull from bunches (grapes), wash, spread on frames until dry.
Figs: All types	
Grapes: All types	
Peaches: All types	Wash, halve or quarter if fruit is large, remove pit (peaches), spread skin side down on frames until dry. DO NOT TURN.
Pears: All types	
Plums: All types	Most plums do not dry well; the prune plum is best. Wash and spread on frames until dry.

How to Build a Juice Press

by F.E. Atkinson and C.C. Strachan

This fruit press design allows anyone who is handy with a few tools to construct a press for home use. The fruit press is primarily designed for apples, but it can be used for pressing any pulped fruit. The grater can be used for any fruits free of large stones. With apples, the fruit press will handle from one to five boxes, yielding 2 to 10 gallons at one pressing.

The essential parts consist of the frame, drainboard, rack, trays, platform, grater, and hopper. It has been found advisable to construct the parts of the press in the order they are listed.

Frame

The four corner posts are made of dressed 4'' x 4'', 47'' long. The dressed size will vary from 3-1/2'' to 3-3/4''. These posts are joined together with 2'' x 4'' braces, placed 12'' from the bottom, and across the top. These are set into the corner posts sufficiently so that their outer surface will be flush with the piece of 3/4'' x 2-1/2'' nailed on to the posts immediately above the lower braces. The 2'' x 4'' braces and the 3/4'' x 2-1/2'' are cut at a 45 degree angle at the corners. The length of these pieces is 28''.

The top 2'' x 4'' braces on both sides of the press are strengthened by 1-1/2'' angle iron 28'' long. Holes large enough for 1/2'' rods are drilled 9-3/8'' (measured to the centre of the hole) from each end. Two pieces of 1-1/2'' angle iron 19-3/4'' long, with similar holes 5-3/8'' from each end, reinforce the lower side braces. Holes are bored in the 2'' x 4'' braces to correspond with the holes in the angle iron. The 1/2'' x 37'' rods are put in place and the nuts tightened until the rods are firm.

The same 2'' x 4'' in the lower group that are drill-ed to accommodate the 1/2'' rods are also notched in four places to take care of the reinforcements on the rack These are illustrated in figure 3. These notches are 1-1/2'' wide, 1-3/4'' deep, and 3/4'' into the 2'' x 4''. Two of these notches are situated 1/8'' from the corner post, while the near side of the other two is 6'' from the corner post.

3-Ply Drainboard

A piece of 3-ply is tightly fitted into the square space developed by the lower 2'' x 4''. This 3-ply is located so that the high side opposite the drain hole is 2'' below the top of the 2'' x 4'' brace, while the side near the outlet hole is 2-1/2'' below the top of the 2'' x 4'' brace. Any rough stripping can be used below the 3-ply to form a ledge, while small right-angled triangles of 3/4'' material can be nailed in the corners for reinforcement. The length of the sides of these triangles on each side of the right angle is the distance from the corner formed by the brace and the corner post to the inside corner of the post. This will be in the neighbourhood of 2-1/2''. A suitable moulding for the top side to seal the joint between the 3-ply, the braces, and corner post may be made by planing 1/2'' x 3/8'' strips to almost a triangle in cross section. The 3-ply catches the juice and delivers it to the 1'' hole in the 2'' x 4'' brace in the front of the press.

Any easily worked metal can be used instead of the 3-ply, provided it is painted with a good paint and thoroughly dried. Four-hour white enamel is suitable.

Rack

The rack is made of 19 pieces of 1'' x 1'' nailed on to four stringers of 1-1/4'' x 1-7/8''. The stringers are spac-ed so that they will fit into the notches previously de-

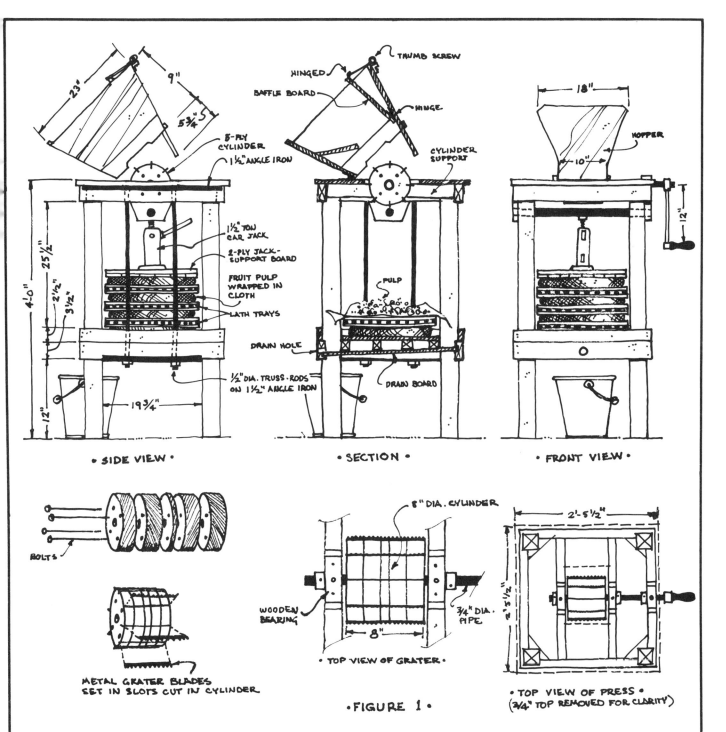

scribed in the side braces. The stringers and the 1'' x 1'' pieces should be made of the strongest wood available, as the rack has to withstand the full pressure of the jack. The two 1'' x 1'' pieces on each side of the rack are cut off flush with the first stringer to allow room for the corner posts. The rack is removable so as to facilitate cleaning.

Lath Trays

Standard laths or wooden strips 3/8'' x 1-1/2'' are cut to a length of 19''. A tray is 19'' square and consists of a single layer of laths placed parallel to one another and the thickness of a lath apart. These laths are crossed at each end (above and below) with laths that hold the

rack together. Copper clout nails, one to a lath, are driven in from both sides. Five lath trays can be used at a time. These are illustrated in figure 2.

Pressure Platform

This is made of three pieces of 1'' x 6'' x 19'' crossed by three other similar pieces. As this platform is subjected to considerable strain, it is wise to nail it thoroughly with nails long enough to clinch.

Wooden Bearings
Grater Supports

Take two pieces of 2'' x 4'' x 25'' for grater supports and bore the bearing holes as directed in the follow-

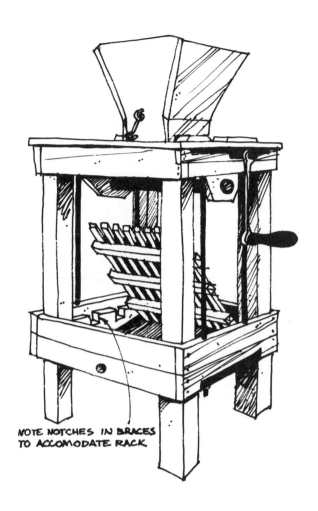

NOTE NOTCHES IN BRACES
TO ACCOMODATE RACK

• FIGURE 2 •

thickness of the board to make 8'', to bolt them together with four bolts countersunk at each end, and to turn the boards into a cylinder 8'' x 8''. A 1'' hole is also drilled through the centre.

The circumference of the cylinder is marked into eigths and lines drawn lengthwise on its surface. On each line a sawcut is made in which the blades will be fitted. The depth of these cuts will depend on the size of blades being used. In seven cuts, pieces of a coarse saw blade (such as a bucksaw or pruning saw) are placed with 3/16'' of teeth protruding from the cylinder. In the remaining cut, the blade is placed down so that a smooth edge protrudes to the same extent as the teeth. An example of the teeth used and also a smooth blade are shown in figure 3.

Shaft

A 23'' piece of 3/4'' pipe is used as a shaft. Quarter-inch holes are drilled at each end of the cylinder so that pins may be inserted to keep the cylinder from turning on the shaft. Collars are also used on the shaft to keep the cylinder properly spaced between the bearings. These collars are 3/4'' lengths of 1'' pipe with a set screw through one side. The bearing caps should be marked so that they will be replaced in the same position as they were originally made.

Hopper

A hopper as illustrated can be built to fit over the grater. Notches are cut out of the sides of the bottom to

ing before nailing them in place. Mark the centres of the 2'' x 4'' and attach 2'' x 2'' x 6'' pieces on the 2'' edge at the centre, using 6'' x 3/8'' bolts at each end of the bearing cap. Bore a 1'' hole at the centre, half in the cap and half in the 2'' x 4''. Quarter-inch oil holes can be bored in the top of each cap. These two pieces of 2'' x 4'' are now nailed lengthwise through the frame braces 8-1/2'' apart. They are 6-1/2'' from the inside of the side 2'' x 4''.

If the hole for the bolt through the bearing cap on the side of the shaft farthest from the drain hole is 1-1/2'' from the centre of the shaft, the end of the bolt may be used to attach the scraper roller later described.

Grater

There are two ways of making this part. The easier is to take a solid piece of wood and turn it down on a lathe or plane it to obtain a cylinder 8'' long and 8'' in diameter. The disadvantage of this method is the possibility of splits developing. The second method is to take sufficient

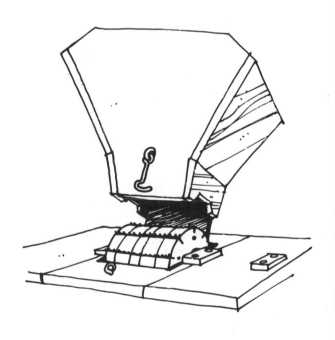

• FIGURE 3 •

fit over the bearing caps. The hopper may be removed to facilitate cleaning by releasing the 4'' hook and eye at each end (figure 2). The baffle board is hinged at the bottom and can be adjusted to different positions by loosening the thumb screw. The lower edge of the baffle board is tapered to a 1/4'' thickness; this taper extends back 2-3/4''. The taper is on the side of the baffle board facing the grater. The purpose of this board is to force apples against the grater. The position in which this board works best will be found in actual operation. If it is not possible to obtain an 8'' piece of flat iron slotted except at each end, with which to adjust the baffle board, then holes may be drilled through the side of the hopper to match a hole in the baffle board, and pegs or nails used to hold the board in different positions.

Top Covering

The top of the press may be covered with any 3/4'' material. The boards covering the side through which the shaft must be notched on the under side so as to fit properly over this item.

Pressure Bar

This is a piece of 1-1/2'' shafting and is sufficiently strong to resist most of the pressures used. However, if sufficient pressure is being used to bend the shaft, then a piece of 4'' x 4'' can be placed on the under side of the shaft. This 4'' x 4'' can be notched so that it fits over the support for the shaft. This notching will prevent the 4'' x 4'' from turning on the shaft.

Scraper Roller

When the grater is turned by hand, there is not sufficient speed to keep it clean. Consequently grated pulp rides around on the cylinder and eventually clogs the throat where apples are ground. To overcome this, a piece of 1/2'' or 3/4'' garden hose 8'' long can be placed on a piece of 3/16'' rod or heavy wire, as illustrated in figure 4. This roller is secured by the nuts of the bearing bolts on the throat side of the grater. The ends of the wire are flattened and slightly bent so as to maintain a small tension against the grater. The hose thus lies lengthwise on the cylinder and scrapes off the pulp. When it is hit by the blades, the hose rolls on the rod. If the grater is driven with an electric motor, the roller *must* be removed as the increased speed causes the rubber to be cut by the blades.

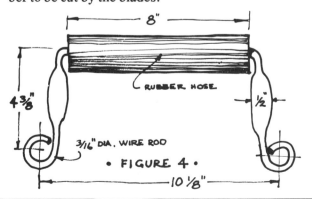

· FIGURE 4 ·

Painting

It is desirable to paint the press with white paint or four hour enamel. This prevents warping and checking of the wood and helps to keep the apparatus clean.

Operation of the Press

Apples are placed in the hopper. A piece of unbleached factory cotton, 36'' x 36'', is placed on the slatted rack, with the corners of the cloth in the middle of the sides of the rack. The apples are grated until the resulting pulp forms a layer 2'' to 3'' thick and 18'' square. The corners of the cloth are then folded over the pulp, completely enclosing the mass. This is commonly called a "cheese". A lath tray is then placed on top of this apple pulp and cloth, and the operation is repeated. If a short jack is used, five cheeses can be pressed at one time, yeilding approximately 10 gallons of juice. The pressure platform is placed on top of the last cheese. The jack is worked between this and the shaft. If this shaft is bent or the jack becomes too short, the piece of 4'' x 4'' previously described can be used. If it's desirable to press only one box of apples, a few pieces of heavy timber can be used on top of the pressure platform to raise the jack up to the shaft.

Where power is available, a 1/3-horsepower motor, 1,750 r.p.m., can be used to turn the grater. A 3'' sheave for a V-belt is placed on the motor and a 12-1/2'' sheave on the grater shaft. An automobile V-shaped fan belt makes a suitable drive. This is illustrated in figure 5. Care should be taken not to feed the apples too fast and not to feed any apples until the grater has been started.

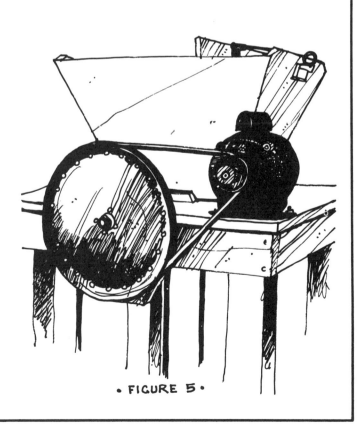

· FIGURE 5 ·

Preserving Juices

Apple Juice

Although there are several methods of preparing sterile sweet apple juice, most of these are too cumbersome or too expensive for use in the home. The following simple method is suggested for home use, where only a few dozen bottles may be desired and no special equipment is available. This method does not give extreme clarity, but it does retain the pleasing flavour and health-giving properties of the fresh juice.

1. Strain the sweet juice. Fill clean beer bottles with juice until they are brimming full.
2. Place a wash-boiler containing 3-1/2 to 4 inches of warm water and a slatted wooden false bottom on the stove. Fill the boiler with the full beer bottles. A full bottle in this case has juice within 1/2 inch of the top of the neck. As the juice expands, the bottle should overflow. If the bottles are stood close together, the boiler should hold 29 to 30 bottles. If the proper amount of water has been used, it should reach halfway up the necks of the bottles.
3. Allow the water in the boiler to heat until it just starts to boil. This is evidenced by the upward movement of the water and the bubbles of steam that reach the surface and burst. Be sure this stage is reached, then move the boiler back to the cooler part of the stove and commence capping the bottles. There should be no air in the bottles when they are capped. If a thermometer is available, a test at the centre of a bottle should show a temperature of 180° F. It is wise to use an aluminum or parchment-spotted cap. These caps are the ordinary crown cap, with a circular disc of aluminum or parchment on the cork. The aluminum or parchment is much easier to sterilize than plain cork.

A handy "gadget" for removing the hot beer bottle from the boiler, and one which can be made from 1/8-inch steel wire, is illustrated in figure 1. In making this holder, two pieces of wire 32 inches long are bent as illustrated in A and B. B is placed beside A and the wires pressed into the open round bends at C. Then the wires E and F are bent at right angles, as illustrated. The open joint at C is next pressed closed with a pair of pliers. Both sets of wires are then bent to form the handles.

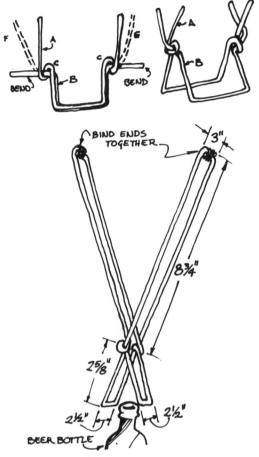

FIGURE 1

In the process of capping, it is wise to lay a few layers of newspaper on the base of the capper to avoid cracking the hot bottles on the cold metal. It is also a good plan to lay newspapers on the table where the hot bottles are to be laid. Lay all bottles on their sides after capping, to sterilize the neck of the bottle and the cap.

Nutritionally, freezing is the best method of preserving. This can be easily done by using old (or new) milk cartons as containers to freeze the juice in.

If you press winter apples and find the juice sour, allow it to sit in crocks of some sort for a short time (2 to 10 days), in order to age before bottling or freezing.

Grape Juice

A very pleasant grape juice may be prepared in the home from any of the American varieties such as Concord. The grapes are removed from the stem and placed in an enamel or aluminum utensil. They are then thoroughly broken to release the juice, and heated to 160° F., a very light simmer, for 10 minutes. This step serves to release the colour from the skin and other soluble solids from the pulp. The resulting juice, pulp, and skins are then passed through a cheesecloth sack. A small sample of the juice should be cooled and tasted for sweetness.

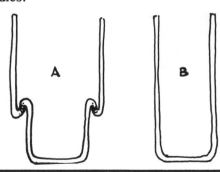

Sometimes as much as one pound of sugar or honey may be needed for every gallon of juice. The sweetener is thoroughly dissolved by stirring. The sweetened juice may then be sterilized in the same manner as described for sweet apple juice. Cream of tartar crystals usually settle on the bottom of the container during storage. These crystals are not harmful.

Juices with Suspended Pulp (Tomato, Apricot, and Prune)

Thoroughly vine-ripened tomatoes are stemmed and cored. The fruit is slightly pulped and placed on the stove in a covered kettle. It is heated to boiling. As much fruit as possible is placed in the kettle at the commencement of this step in order to exclude the air and prevent destruction of vitamin C. After the pulp has boiled four to five minutes, it is ready to be passed through a sieve to remove the skin and seeds. At this point, the necessity of haste cannot be over-emphasized, as the juice will lose much of its vitamin value if exposed to the air. If the juice is kept near the boiling point, the vapour given off during the extracting will keep the air away from the product.

Return the extracted juice to the kettle and bring just to boiling. At the same time, have enough sealers or beer bottles being kept hot in the oven. Fill these with juice, seal, and place in boiling water. If the juice is kept hot, beer bottles may be filled to within one inch of the top of the bottle. If beer bottles are used, sterilize caps in boiling water for five minutes before use. Aluminum or parchment spotted caps do not require this treatment. Cook beer bottles on their sides for 10 minutes in boiling water. Quart sealers should receive 20 minutes cooking.

Apricot juice and prune juice can be made similarly to tomato. The addition of a little water to the pulped apricot or prunes just prior to heating will reduce any tendency to scorching. About two to three cups of water to each 10 pounds of fruit is normally sufficient. Apricot can be sweetened by adding about 1-1/2 to 2 pounds of sugar or honey to each 10 pounds or gallon of cooked pulp. Dilute one to one with water before use. Prune juice, if made from thoroughly ripened fruit, does not require additional sweetner.

Extractor for Juice with Suspended Pulp

This extractor (fig. 2) is simple to make and can be used for any of the juices containing pulp. The size will depend on the utensils with which it is to be used.

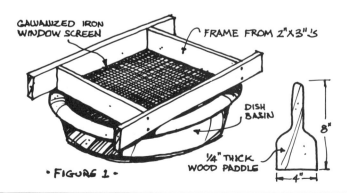

· FIGURE 1 ·

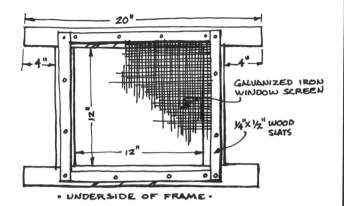

· UNDERSIDE OF FRAME ·

· FIGURE 2 ·

Making Vinegar

The process of making vinegar consists of two distinct steps; namely, the fermentation of the fresh juice and the acetification of the fermented juice.

Fermentation

1. Use a clean sound barrel, cask, or crock. Scrub with scalding water and lye if the container is not new.

2. Fill with fresh juice and add one yeast cake to every five gallons.

3. Fermentation will be complete when the small bubbles stop rising to the surface.

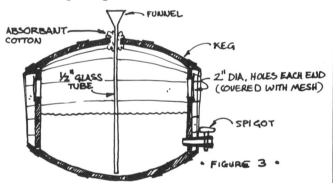

· FIGURE 3 ·

Acetification

A 10-gallon keg is a suitable container in which to conduct the process of acetification. Place the keg on its side and bore a two-inch hole near the top of each end. Screen these openings with wire to prevent entrance of insects, while permitting passage of air. A spigot should be placed in one end of the keg near the bottom. The fermented juice, to which some old vinegar or "mother" has been added, is then poured in through a funnel, as shown in figure 8, until the keg is half full. This apparatus works best when placed in a location where a temperature of at least 70°F. is maintained. If trouble is encountered from the staves on the top side of the keg "drying out", the apparatus can be arranged so that the same system is used, but the keg is kept in an upright position and filled only half full.

Finished vinegar should be ready in six weeks. As it is drawn off, more of the fermented juice may be added. Small batches may be finished in crocks or open casks.

The Smoke Curing and Salting of Fish

by Iola I. Berg

The curing of fishery products by smoking has been carried out for many centuries. It's known that early man used a wood smoke cure in the preservation of fish and meat. The original method has come down to the present day only slightly altered. The quality of the finished product is still largely dependent on the skill and experience of the operator. Take *caution* because the processes described herein *may not* kill or render harmless all possilbe natural toxins or disease-causing organisms.

Smoke Curing Principles

Smoke curing involves the following processes: (1) salting, (2) drying, (3) heat treatment, (4) smoking. The final result of the product depends on the proper care and control of each of these processes, and upon the original quality and species of fish to be smoked.

Salting the product prior to smoking is usually done by soaking in brine for a definite length of time. The strength of the brine determines the type of cure of the product. Brining the fish is important; it firms the fish by removing moisture. Salt also imparts a flavour to the product. Fish may be lightly or heavily brined, depending upon the type of product desired. Lightly salted fish shor ɪd be smoked immediately, since brining merely serves to impart flavour to the fish and to firm the flesh. Heavy brining is used in the development of special cures; for example, in the mild curing of salmon and also for preserving fish until the smoke curing process can be applied. The salt concentration reaches about 8 or 10 per cent, but it is not sufficient to preserve the fish indefinitely; thus the product must be kept in cold storage, preferably about 32 to 34 degrees F. Most of this salt must be removed from the fish prior to smoking. This is done by soaking the fish in cold running water.

Smokehouses

Simple smokehouses: There are three types of simple smokehouses that may be built cheaply and easily.

(1) *Converted icebox or refrigerator*: Drill some holes at the top to allow the smoke to escape. Use a hotplate at the bottom, preferably one with a temperature control. This provides a better control for hot smoking. Run a cord through the drain if an icebox is used. Into an old large pot, place a few pieces of alder to smoulder.

(2) *Oil drum, screen, and washtub*: Use a 50-gallon oil or gas drum with the top and bottom cut out. Set a three-foot square, one-half-inch wire-mesh galvanized screen on top of the drum. Place the fish on the screen and put an old washtub, upside down, over the fish. Then punch a few nail holes in the bottom of the washtub.

After suitable brining and soaking, the fish is subjected to a drying process. This is necessary to remove additional moisture from the fish. The more moisture removed from the fish, the greater will be the keeping quality. Drying is usually done outdoors, but can be done in the smokehouse. Maintenance of the proper humidity is quite important. Relative humidity should be below 75 per cent. Drying aids in the formation of the "pellicle." The pellicle is the glossy, firm surface imparted to the fish, which gives it the desired appearance and allows for the development and absorption of the delicate smoke flavour. Thus the formation of the pellicle is quite important in obtaining a good product.

The fish may be smoked in a cold or hot atmosphere. For cold-smoking, the temperature is held below 85° F. For hot-smoking, it may range from 120° to 180° F. and may be eaten immediately. It does not have good keeping qualities when cured by the hot method. Smoked fishery products are highly perishable and should be held under refrigeration at all times. For smoking most any kind of hardwood may be used, such as oak, alder, hickory, and mahogany. Alder is most commonly used in the Pacific Northwest. The soft woods are not recommended because of their resinous nature; they give an acrid flavour and odour to the product.

Some fish contain different amounts of fat or oil, and their salting and smoke curing may need to be adjusted accordingly. Small size fish may require as much smoke as a larger size fish of the same type, but the amount of drying may be varied. Those fishery products smoked prior to canning are smoked only lightly, just sufficient to produce the desired smoke flavour.

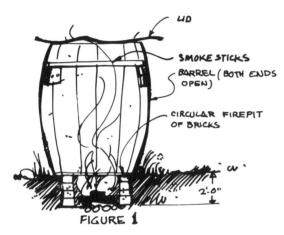

FIGURE 1

(3) *Barrel types (fig. 1)*: Knock the ends out of a large barrel, set it over a hole in the ground about two feet deep and a little narrower in width than the diameter of the barrel, and nail wooden strips in the barrel on two sides a few inches below the top. The ends of the smokesticks rest on these strips. Place a loosely-fitting cover on top (fig. 2). Dig a hole adjacent to the bottom of the barrel, connected with the pit, and fit it with a cover. The fire is fed through this hole, which also serves as a draft when the lid is partly raised. A smokehouse so constructed is best for hot smoking, but it may be used for cold-smoking if operated carefully. If the fire is permitted to flare up, however, the fish may be scorched. It is best to dig the fire pot on the side from which the prevailing winds come (fig. 2).

In hot smoking, the fish are hung near the fire, usually not more than three or four feet distant, and smoked at temperatures from 120 to 180 degrees, so they are partially or wholly cooked. In cold smoking, the fish are hung at some distance from a low smouldering fire and cured at temperatures usually lower than 90 degrees F. The degree of preservation depends on the length of time the fish are smoked; fish cold-smoked for a few hours, for example, will keep only a short time. If an extended period of preservation is desired, fish must be cold-smoked from a few days to a week or more.

Permanent Smokehouses (fig. 3)

(1) If a more permanent smokehouse is desired, and one that will handle a larger amount of fish, make a little shed, seven feet high and four feet square, inside measurement. About 12 inches above the ground, place a false bottom with 3/4 or one-inch auger holes at two-inch intervals. On the two sides, wooden battens are nailed at one-foot intervals, the first about 18 inches below the top. The ends of the smokesticks on which the fish are hung rest on these battens. The whole front of the house is hinged for a door. Three or four holes about two inches square are cut on the two sides a few inches below the roof, with slides to cover, for use as drafts or ventilators. The pit below the smokehouse and the fire pit may be lined with brick. A terracotta drain pipe may be placed in the trench connecting the two pits to act as a chimney.

(2) Smokehouse with the fire box removed from the house (fig. 4). In cold-smoking, it is preferable to have the firebox removed from the house, and the smoke conveyed through an underground pipe ending in an elbow joint in the bottom of the smokehouse. A common stovepipe damper is placed in the middle joint of pipe, the ordinary handle being fitted above when the pipe is covered with earth. This damper is the principal fire and smoke control.

A nice feature is added by the use of a "smoke spreader," which is a rectangular galvanized-iron box, one foot square and two feet high, open at the bottom. Numerous 3/4-inch holes punched in the sides and top permit the escape of smoke. This box is placed directly over the mouth of the elbow and causes an even distribution of smoke throughout the house. It serves also to pre-

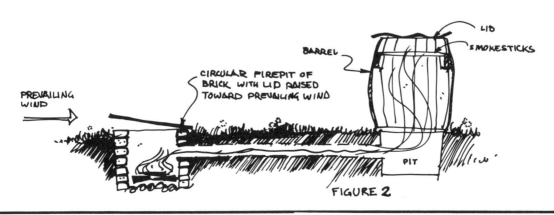

FIGURE 2

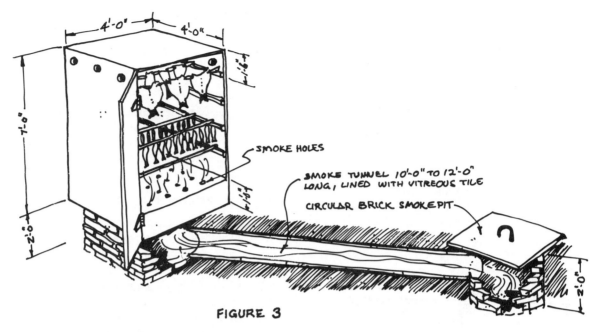

FIGURE 3

vent scorching of fish by direct draft, if at certain stages considerable heat is applied. The arrangement of fire box, smoke flue, and smoke spreader is made clear by the accompanying figures, which also illustrate (fig. 4) other possible modifications, such as construction of wood sliding trays and tip ventilator in roof. The screen trays should never be used if the fish can be suspended from rods, since the impression of the screen wire detracts from the appearance of the fish. In cold or rainy weather, condensation of moisture on the underside of the roof may occur, so that the dripping of water on the fish may injure the appearance, though not the quality, of the product. This difficulty has been overcome by stretching a double thickness of burlap just beneath the top. This has the double effect of reducing condensation and of absorbing the moisture as it is condensed.

Methods of Hanging Fish for Smoking

The fish may be hung on one or more S-shaped iron hooks, which are in turn hung over sticks running from one side of the smokehouse to the other. If whole, they may be hung on round wooden sticks inserted under the gill flap and through the mouth. When these sticks have been hung with fish, they are suspended from one side to the other of the smokehouse. If the fish are split, the smoke-sticks may be two-inch square sticks. Nails are driven through two sides at a 45-degree angle at intervals, depending on the average size of the fish smoked. The sides of the fish are hung on adjacent nail-points, just below the bony neck plate, thus holding the fish open so that all of the flesh surface will be smoked. Another method is to run 14-inch iron rods through the fish

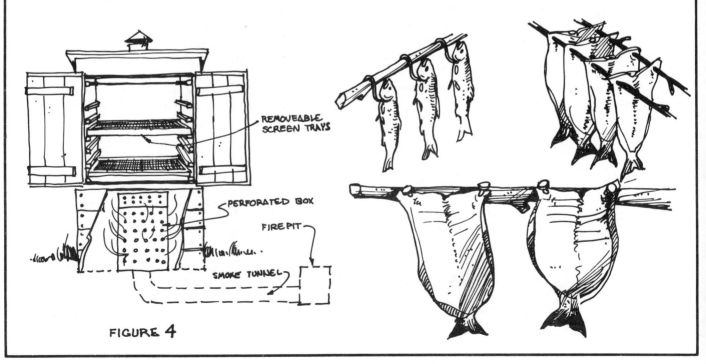

FIGURE 4

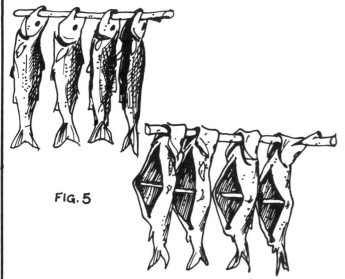

FIG. 5

just under the hard bony plate at the neck, one rod on each side. Thus, each fish hangs from two rods. Twelve or more fish may be hung on a set of two rods four feet long. Fillets may be hung over three-sided sticks of wood which, in turn, rest upon the sticks at each side of the smokehouse.

Do not crowd the fish in placing or hanging them in the smokehouse.

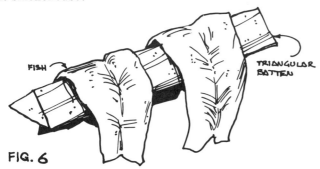

FISH

TRIANGULAR BATTEN

FIG. 6

Hot smoking

General method: This process may be used with almost any species, herring, shad, trout, etc. This method is recommended if it is desired to prepare a fish that can be used immediately without cooking. It may be kept longer without molding or souring, but even so, it will preserve for only a short time.

Split the fish along the back, just above the backbone, so that it will open in one piece, leaving the belly solid. Scrape out all viscera, blood, and membrane. Make an additional cut under the backbone for smaller fish. For the larger fish, cut out the forward three-fifths of the backbone. Wash thoroughly and soak in a 70-degree salt brine (one-half cup salt to one quart water) for 30 minutes to leach out blood in the flesh. Then prepare a brine using the following ingredients: 2 lbs. salt (use a fine grade of salt or sea salt), 1 lb. sugar (don't know how honey would work, but it's certainly worth trying), 1 oz. crushed black peppers, and 1 oz. crushed bay leaves. This is made up into a 90-degree brine solution. The amounts of ingredients are increased in proportion to the amount of brine to be made. Spices may be increased or decreased according to individual taste.

The fish are held in the brine for periods of from two to four hours, depending upon their thickness, and the desire for a lightly or heavily cured fish. Weather conditions also make a difference; the exact length of time must be determined by experiment. Rinse off the fish in cold, fresh water and hang outside in a cool, shady and breezy place to dry for about three hours before hanging in the smokehouse, or until a thin shiny "skin" or pellicle has formed on the surface.

For the first eight hours, keep the fire low and smoldering during the smoking process. The temperature should then be built up. After four hours of heavy smoking, the fire is increased until the temperature is between 130 and 150 degrees F. The fish are cured at this temperature for two to three hours, or until they have a glossy, brown surface. This partially cooks, or hot-smokes the fish.

When smoking is finished, the fish must be cooled for two or three hours. They may be brushed over lightly with vegetable oil (usually cottonseed) while warm. This is sometimes done just after finishing the cold-smoking part of the process, before the temperature is increased. This gives a more attractive appearance and a light protective coating. For a better coating, the fish may be dipped in melted paraffin, but this coating is brittle and the fish must be handled carefully and the paraffin removed before eating. Each fish should be wrapped in wax paper and stored in the refrigerator. Spoilage occurs more rapidly if the fish are stored in a warm place or a cold damp place.

Cold smoking

General method: Small fish, such as herring may be cold-smoked in the round (without cleaning), but they should be gibbed. Gibbing is making a small cut just below the gills and hulling out the gills, heart, liver and leaving the belly uncut. Fish larger than 1 pound should be split along the back to lie flat in a single piece, leaving the belly portion uncut. All traces of blood, black skin, and viscera must be removed, paying special attention to the area just under the backbone. The head does not need to be removed. If the head is cut off, the hard bony plate just below the gills is allowed to remain, as it will be needed to carry the weight of the fish when they are hung in the smokehouse.

Wash the fish thoroughly, and place them in a brine made in the proportion of 1 cup of salt to one gallon of water. They should be left in the brine at least 30 minutes to soak out the blood diffused through the flesh. At the end of this time, rinse in fresh cold water and drain for a few minutes.

Each fish is dropped singularly in a shallow box of fine salt and dredged thoroughly. The fish are picked up with as much salt as will cling to the body, and packed in even layers in a box or wooden tub. A small amount of salt may be scattered between each layer. The fish are left in salt from 1 to 12 hours depending upon weather, size of fish, fatness, length of time for which preservation is desired, and whether the fish are split or round.

Salting is an important and essential feature in smoking, as smoking is not a sufficient preservative in itself. Unsalted fish will usually sour or spoil under temperature and humidity conditions found in the smokehouse before they can be cured. Fish such as halibut, herring, mackerel, or salmon may be smoked after being held in salt for a year. In these cases, the excess salt is removed by soaking the fish in fresh water. Fish given a heavy salt-cure and held in storage for some time before smoking are not so desirable in quality as those given a light salting and smoked immediately.

When the fish are taken out of the salt, they should be scrubbed off. They are hung to dry in the shed, as direct sunlight causes rusting of the fish. If the fish are kept shaded in a breezy location, they will dry well with a clear colour. If only a few fish are being dried, they may be hung in a shady undercover area where there is good cross-ventilation. An electric fan may be used if there is not much breeze. Drying racks may be made with chicken wire; the fish are placed skin side down and turned. They will dry on both sides, but the impression of the wire detracts from the appearance. The fish is dried until a thin skin, or pellicle, is formed on the surface. This should take about three hours under average conditions. If smoking is begun while the skin is still moist, the time required is longer, the colour will not be as desirable, the fish will not have as good a surface, and will steam and soften in smoking. In damp weather, fish are sometimes dried by hanging in the smokehouse over a low clear fire with little smoke, but the use of electric fans or blowers is a better procedure. A low smouldering fire is started an hour or two before the fish are hung in the smokehouse. The fire must not give off too much smoke during the first 8 to 12 hours if the total cure is 24 hours, or for the first 24 hours, if the cure is longer. The temperature in the smokehouse should not be higher than 90 degrees F. in California or the southern states, or 70 degrees F. in northern states, the Pacific Northwest, and Canada. If available a thermometer should be used in controlling smokehouse temperature; if not, a simple test is to insert the hand in the smokehouse—if the air feels distinctly warm, the temperature is too high. When the first part of the smoking process is ended, a dense smoke may be built up and maintained for the balance of the cure. If the fish are to be kept for about two weeks, they should be smoked for 24 hours; if for a longer time, smoking may require five days or more. Hard-smoked herring may require three or four weeks.

A few general rules must be followed in tending the fire. It must be kept low and steady; where hardwood sawdust is not available, chips and bark do almost as well. The fire must not be allowed to die out at night, nor should it be built up before leaving, as this will create too much heat. It must be tended regularly during the night. The general method of cold-smoking may be used with most fish, if the proper consideration is given to size, climate, humidity, salting, and other limiting factors.

Fillets: Any white-fleshed, "lean" fish which will produce fillets weighing more than one pound may be used. Cut the fish in fillets, removing the backbone and skin. Cover with a 90-degree brine and hold for two hours. Remove and drain for 10 to 15 minutes and air dry for two hours. Hang across a three-sided smoke-stick. Cure over a fire with a fairly light smoke for four hours at a temperature not higher than 90 degrees F. Turn the fillets so that the side resting on the smoke-stick is uppermost and smoke four hours longer. Smother the fire so that a dense cloud of smoke is obtained and smoke until the fillets are a deep straw yellow, turning the fillets once or twice so that both sides will be evenly coloured. This operation should take about six hours. Cool the fillets and wrap each separately in waxed paper. Store in a cool, dry place. They will keep about ten days.

Salmon: All species of salmon, steelhead, and lake trout may be smoked. The general cold-smoking method is most commonly used, but the following method gives a more appetizing product.

The heads should be cut off and the fish gutted. They must be split into two sides, and the backbone removed. To do this, the shoulder of the salmon is forced down on a sharp-pointed nail protruding from the cleaning table to prevent slipping. Short incisions are made under the anal fin, just above and below the backbone. With the upper lug or shoulder tip held by the left hand, enter the knife at the shoulder above the backbone, holding the blade steady, with the edge at a slight downward angle touching the bone. Take the whole side off with one sweep of the knife. If the work has been done well, little flesh will be left on the backbone; the side will be smooth. A thin line of backbone edge should run down the centre of the side. To remove the second side, a cut is made at the shoulder just under the backbone. With the edge of the knife blade resting against the backbone at a slight upward angle, give one sweep of the knife down to the root of the tail. This separates the backbone from the flesh without removing the fish from the nail. The two sides should be similar.

The sides are washed thoroughly and trimmed of ragged edges and blood clots. Blood remaining in the veins along the belly cavity should be removed by pressing it toward the back, either with the fingers or the blade of the knife. If the blood is not removed, it will harden and discolour the flesh. The sides are placed in a tub of 90-degree salinometer brine (a saturated salt solution) and chilled with ice. This removes diffused blood, makes the sides a little firmer, and stops oil from oozing out of the flesh. The fish should remain in the brine for 60 to 90 minutes.

The sides should be drained for 15 to 20 minutes. A shallow box is filled with a salting mixture made in the following proportions:

2 lbs. salt
1 lb. brown sugar
1 oz. saltpeter
1 oz. white pepper
1 oz. crushed bay leaves
1 oz. allspice
1 oz. crushed cloves
1 oz. crushed mace

This amount should be enough for about 20 pounds of fish. The salmon is placed in the box, one side at a time, and dredged in the mixture, which is rubbed lightly into the flesh. The sides are packed in a tub or other suitable container with as much of the curing mixture as will cling to the flesh. A loose-fitting cover is placed on it and weighted down.

The fish are left for 8 to 12 hours, then rinsed and scrubbed to remove all traces of the salting mixture. The sides are fixed on hangers and dried in the air for six hours. If air drying conditions are not favourable, fans may be used. Hang the fish in the smokehouse and smoke in a gentle heat (not more than 100 degrees F.) for eight hours. Build up a dense smoke and continue the cure for 16 to 24 hours at a temperature not higher than 70 degrees F. To obtain a product having the maximum of preservation, the second part of the smoking period should be 48 hours.

The fish should be allowed to cool for several hours before handling, then brushed with vegetable oil, and stored in a cool, dry place.

Smoking Fish Indian Fashion

This will keep two weeks to one month in good condition. This method is especially recommended for trout, pike, or pickerel.

Cut off the heads, and gut the fish. A cut is made above the backbone almost to the tail. Another cut is made under the backbone, which is broken off, leaving not more than one-fifth of the tail section uncut. The fish should lie flat in one piece. The flesh is scored longitudinally from head to tail, with the cuts about one-half inch deep and one inch apart. After washing thoroughly and wiping dry, the fish are rubbed inside and out with a mixture of 1 oz. pepper to 1 oz. salt.

The fish are stored in a cool place overnight, and next morning are rinsed carefully. Two or three thin, flat wooden sticks are fastened across the back to keep the fish spread open. The roughly-pointed sticks pass through the skin. Dry the fish in a breezy place until the surface moisture has dried and a thin skin has formed on the surface.

A shallow fire pit is dug, about three feet in diameter, and a fire is started while the fish are drying, so that a good bed of red coals will be ready immediately. Hardwood should be used. When the fish have dried, about three hours under average conditions, each fish is fastened to the forked end of a stick about four to five feet in length. The other end of the stick is thrust into the

ground, so that it hangs over the bed of coals at an angle. The sticks should be placed so the fish will not touch each other

Two or three fish may be fastened across a stick, and thrust into the ground as in the first method, but must not be placed as close to the fire.

A tripod of poles is then erected above the smoke-sticks; on this is laid a thick thatching of green boughs and grass. A hole may be left in the thatching near the ground. Green wood is then placed on the coals, building up a dense smoke, and the hole is covered. It will be necessary to place additional green wood on the fire from time to time. The fish are smoked from six to eighteen hours, depending on size and degree of smoke-cure desired.

After cooling, the smoked fish are wrapped and stored in a cool, dry place.

Smoked Oysters

Shuck fresh oyster, drain thoroughly and dry on absorbent paper. Place the oysters on an oiled smoking rack, without overlapping, and cold-smoke for about 1 hour, or until oysters have taken on colour and their edges are curled and golden brown.

A Cardboard Smokehouse: Easy to Make

Anyone who can use a knife, saw, and hammer can make a low-cost smokehouse from a cardboard carton (fig. 7). It can be folded flat and moved easily. It is efficient and easy to operate. Its only disadvantage is that it cannot be exposed to rain. A 30-inch square smokehouse holds about 60 pounds of split fish.

Building the Smokehouse

Use a cardboard carton which is about 30 inches square and 48 inches high. Other sizes may be used, but they should be at least 25 inches wide and deep and 40 inches high.

(1) Remove one end by cutting along the edge folds. The open end is used as the bottom.

(2) Unfasten the flaps at the other end, so that they can be bent back and folded together again to make a cover.

(3) If the box is weak and tends to buckle when pressure is applied at the top, strengthen it by tacking a three-quarter-inch strip of wood vertically on the outside at each corner; attach the strip by driving large-head roofing nails (three-quarter inch or 2 centimeters) into them from the inside. Nail four more strips horizontally on the outside on opposite sides; nail two of them four inches from the top and the other two twenty inches from the bottom, driving large-headed roofing nails into them from the inside.

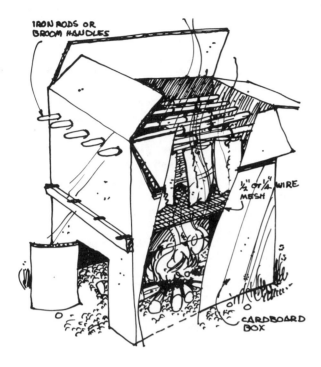

IRON RODS OR BROOM HANDLES

½" OT ¼" WIRE MESH

CARDBOARD BOX

(4) Cut a door 10 inches wide and 12 inches high in the centre of one side at the bottom. Make two cuts, one vertical and one horizontal. The door can then be bent out, with the cardboard on the uncut side acting as a hinge.

(5) Cut holes for the rods (which should extend at least two inches beyond the outside of the carton). Seven rods are used with a 30-inch size carton:

Two rods just below the fold at the top, to keep the flaps from sagging.

Three rods just above the upper horizontal wood strips, to support the fish. The two outside holes are six inches in from the corners, the third is in the centre. (Smaller cartons may need only two rods here.)

Two rods just above the lower horizontal wood strips, to support a tray to catch any fish that falls.

(6) Make a tray by cutting half-inch or quarter-inch wire mesh to fit inside the box. Bend the edges over and hammer them down flat.

(7) Make hooks from pieces of 8 - or 10-guage steel wire 14 inches long (or heavy wire coat hangers). Bend each piece in the middle around a hammer handle or a broomstick. Then, bend the hook end the same way to form a goose neck. The opening of the hook must be big enough to slip easily over the rod; the end must be bent so it will not slip off the rod during the smoking process.

(8) When the right size carton is not available, use two cartons of equal size, at least 24 inches high and 24 inches wide:

(a) Remove the top and bottom from one.

(b) Cut away the bottom of the other.

(c) Telescope the second over the first to get the desired height.

(d) Tack strips of wood on the outside of all four sides of the overlapping space to prevent further telescoping

and to seal the smokehouse.

Smoking

It takes five to six hours to smoke fish ready to eat. The exact period depends on the size of the fish.

The carton will not catch fire if:

(1) The ventilation is controlled to make the fire smoke rather than blaze.

(2) Not too much wood is placed on the fire. If too large a blaze develops, it can be smothered with sawdust or reduced by removing some of the blazing wood.

The fire should be built on a level plot of ground.

How to Salt Fish

By Daniel Casper

Salting, one of the oldest methods of preserving food, is an art as well as a science. The process of salting fish is influenced by weather, size and species of fish, and the quality of salt used. Therefore, experience is needed to adapt the process outlined here to your own situation. Start by salting small lots of different varieties of fish— whatever is available. By salting small amounts of fish at first, you will learn how much time is required for each step. Salted fish, if properly packed to protect it from excessive moisture, will not spoil.

Quality and Cleanliness

There are two things that are of special importance:

(1) The quality of the fish to be salted. The fish must be top quality. Salting will not help poor quality, old, or rotten fish.

(2) Cleanliness in all operations. All water used must be removed from working and drying areas. Whatever comes in contact with the fish, including all the equipment, must be kept clean.

One word of *caution:* Start by salting non-fatty, white-meated varieties of fish. The salting of fatty fish brings up problems of rancidity, rusting, and spoilage which can be handled better after you have experience in salting.

Salting the Fish

The process of salting fish has four operations: (1) Preparing the fish, (2) salting, (3) washing and drying to remove excess salt, and (4) air drying.

Preparing the Fish

The fish should be gutted and beheaded as soon as possible after catching.

(1) Remove the head by cutting on a slanted line following the gills. Sharks can be beheaded at the last line of gill slits. Fish which weigh one-half pound do not have to be beheaded, but they generally should be gutted.

(2) In gutting a fish, cut from the gill cavity along the ventral fold to the anal vent (fig. 1). All the guts must be removed. It is also good practice to remove the black membrane located in the visceral cavity (the hollow in the body of the fish which contains the guts) of many species.

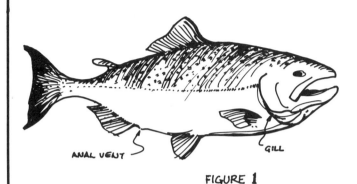

FIGURE 1

(3) All species of fish must be thoroughly bled. If the head has not been removed, cut the throat. Then remove the gills and all blood vessels. Blood clots can cause discolouration as well as bacterial infection which would make the fish unfit for eating.

(4) The shape into which the fish is cut depends on local custom. For a rule of thumb, under 1 pound, the fish may be left whole; from 1 to 10 pounds it should be split in half from head to tail (fig. 2); over 10 pounds, split the fish in two again from head to tail. The collarbone behind the gills should be left intact when a fish is split in half.

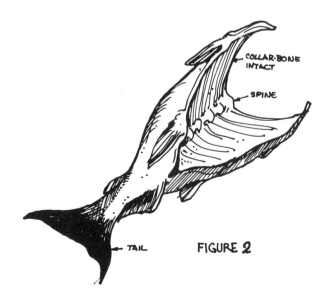

FIGURE 2

Salting

(1) Sprinkle a thin layer of salt, just enough to completely cover the bottom of a waterproof vat.

(2) Place a layer of fish, flesh side up, with enough room for each fish to avoid overlapping. Try for a neat pattern, alternating head to tail and tail to head.

(3) Cover the fish with salt—a thin layer, but with no open spaces.

(4) Repeat steps 2 and 3 up to two or three layers of fish from the top of the vat.

(5) Reverse the fish, packing them *skin* side up to the top of the vat, alternating with layers of salt. The top layer must be salt.

(6) The salt will extract moisture from the fish, forming a brine. Use boards and weights to keep all the fish under the salt.

(7) The brine must be kept saturated (90—degree salinometer—or when no more salt can be dissolved) at all times. As moisture is extracted, more salt must be added to keep the brine saturated. Too little salt will cause the fish to spoil. Too much will detract from the flavour and cause dehydration.

(8) As moisture is extracted from the fish, the level of fish in the vat will fall. More fish can be added—skin side up—alternating a layer of fish with a layer of salt, the top layer always being salt. Continue to add salt to keep the brine saturated.

(9) The fish are "struck through," or thoroughly impregnated with salt, in 12 to 15 days in warm weather. In cold weather the fish should stay in the brine for 21 days or more. The higher the temperature, the quicker the fish will be struck through. When properly salted, the flesh of the fish is translucent. It is firm but yields to gentle pressure, and has a whitish salt cover. An odour of fish and brine should prevail. There should be no spoilage odours.

Washing and Drying to Remove Excess Salt

(1) When the fish are struck through, they are removed from the vat and washed in unpolluted sea water or fresh brine to remove excess salt.

(2) Then place the fish on flat surfaces, using any arrangement of boards and weights to press them—as flat as possible—in order to:

(a) remove excess moisture and

(b) make the fish thinner, which will reduce the length of the air-drying process and improve the appearance of the fish.

Air Drying

(1) The final drying can be done either by sunlight and natural air currents or by artificial heat and air currents generated by fans. In most areas, in the proper season, drying can be done outdoors in the sun and fresh air. Choose an open area to get the most sunlight and wind. Avoid swampy areas, locations near human or animal waste, and especially fly-breeding areas.

(2) When freshly salted fish is first brought out to dry, there is danger of sunburn. If the fish is exposed at this stage to direct sunlight, it may harden on the outside and turn yellow. This will keep the inside from drying properly. To avoid this, keep the fish under shade or semi-shade for the first day.

(3) After the first day, expose the fish to as much sunlight and wind as possible. One method is to lay the fish on triangular slats—so that it rests on the least possible amount of surface—flesh side facing the sun (fig. 3). Another method is to hang the fish by the tail (fig. 4).

(4) Protect the drying fish against dampness. The fish can be moved into small roofed sheds built nearby for protection from rainfall and night-time dampness. The fish should be free of discolouration, mold, or other defects. Split fish should not have ragged edges.

(5) Generally, six warm days with winds of more than three miles per hour should dry the fish enough to prevent spoiling in storage or shipping, provided the fish is properly packed to protect it from excessive moisture.

Using Salted Fish

Salted fish is usually soaked overnight, with at least one change of water, to remove most of the salt before it is eaten. The longer it is soaked, the more salt is removed. Then it is used in the same way as fresh fish, except that it is not good for frying.

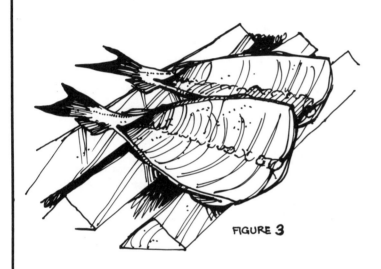

FIGURE 3

• FIGURE 4 •

Cheese Making

Cheesemaking is simple and lots of good fun. All you need is plain old milk. To produce a superior product, always be sure to use raw milk. Cheese can be made from top milk, bottom milk, fresh milk, sour milk, buttermilk, and even from the whey. Goat, cow, and ewe's milk are most common, although in some places the milk of the camel, the water buffalo, the donkey, and the mare are used.

Rennet is an animal product made from the stomach acid of young calves. When added to the milk, it causes the liquid to separate from the solid, thus "curds and whey." If the milk is cold and sweet, the curds are harder. (Extracts of the wild thistle and wild artichoke will also coagulate the milk). The extract of bruised marigold petals has been used for centuries in Europe to add a golden colour to cheese. After the curd has separated, the cheese goes through a drainage process. The process depends on the cheese you are making. Some cheeses are salted and eaten right away, such as ricotta. Another cheese is cut, kneaded, cooked, pressed, ground, and pressed again. This is called cheddaring. After the drainage process, the cheese may be ripened. This final stage varies greatly from cheese to cheese. Bleu cheese, which is originally made from ewe's milk, is innoculated with mold, and within a few months the characteristic green veins have found their way deep in the cheese. Bannon, a French goat cheese, is cured in chestnut leaves, dried, passed through the dregs of wine casks, and fermented in stone crocks. It is finally presented wrapped in fresh chestnut leaves. Prestost, a hard Swedish cheese, is washed in whiskey for five months during curing. Another French goat cheese, Selles-Sur Cher, is kneaded in charcoal until it takes a gray colour, and is then aged slowly. There are hundreds of thousands of different cheeses in the world. Each is part of its native soil—each is unique. Cheese is one of the most ancient foods manufactured by man. Simple and natural, cheese is a gift of the land, and of the slow, seasoned rhythm of country life.

Recipe for Basic Hard Cheese

8 qts. milk . . . 2 lbs. cheese

Allow 4 qts. to sour at room temperature overnight. In the morning, add 4 qts. fresh milk and heat on the stove to lukewarm. Add solution from one-half rennet tablet. (Solution is made by crushing and dissolving tablet in 2 tbsp. cold water.) Let stand until a smooth curd forms (45 minutes). Cut curd into small chunks with a knife. Gently stir with your hand; cut big chunks you may have missed. *Do not* squash the curds. Do this for about 15 minutes. Now, slowly heat the curds and whey to as hot as the hand can stand, stirring constantly. A very firm curd will form. Remove from the heat. Put somewhere to cool, stirring occasionally. When cold, pour curds into cheesecloth, salt to taste, hang to drain. Dress, press, wax, and store.

Bleu Cheese Culture

Take a culture of mold from aged bleu cheese and put it on a loaf of bread. Keep in a moist, dark place for 6 weeks. When the bread has crumbled completely and the mold has separated, dry the mold into a powder. Bottle and cork tightly.

To Use: sprinkle dried mold on the cheese, or pierce it in on the head of a needle in several places. Salt lightly, and let it rest for several days. When the mold has had a good start, pierce it at least 60 times to give air to the mold deep in the interior. Keep in a cool, dark place. Age 2 to 5 months.

Italian Cheese

Heat 10 qts. of fresh milk to 85 degrees. Add solution from one rennet tablet. Let stand until a firm curd forms (45 minutes). Break up curd with hands; heat slowly, stirring constantly, to as hot as the hand can stand. Gather curd in the hands and knead to form a firm ball. (Ricotta Romano is made at this time). Return to whey, and set somewhere to cool. Drain, press, wax, and store.

Ricotta Romano

Before Italian cheese is put back in the whey, heat the whey until a coat of cream rises to the top. Add one qt. milk (per 10 qt.), stir; heat until almost boiling. When curd rises, add one cup strong vinegar. Stir well; curd will come together. Drain curd, salt to taste, serve fresh.

Devonshire Cream

Allow the cream of whole milk to rise. Heat slowly to just below the boiling point. When the layer of cream is firm, skim it and place in a mould to harden.

Pennsylvania Pot Cheese

Prepare the curd from bottom milk. Drain, and grind in a meatgrinder; place in a covered crock. Keep curd warm for several days until it is covered with a tangled mass of mold. Remove curd. Heat slowly for about half an hour in water (or whey), stirring constantly. When it reaches the consistency of honey, put in moulds and cool.

Neufchatel Cheese

From whole goat's milk we make a soft cheese called Neufchatel, similar in appearance and method to cottage cheese, but much richer. Pressed, it makes delicious sandwich spread on wholewheat or rye bread for a cool lunch in hot weather.

Put one gallon of sweet, whole goat's milk in a larger kettle containing water at 72 degrees F. When the milk reaches 70 degrees (use a dairy or candy thermometer), add one Junket rennet tablet dissolved in ¼ cup cold water, and stir this in thoroughly. All utensils that come in contact with the milk should be scalded to kill unwanted bacteria or the flavour of the cheese will be ruined.

The warm milk should set overnight (12 to 15 hours). In the morning the curd will be firm and smooth, with a little whey on top. Spread a clean drain cloth (cheesecloth) over a colander and ladle the curd onto it. Tie the ends of the cloth together and hang the bundle up to drain. I tie mine to the water faucet. It is best to catch the whey and use it (or feed to the livestock). It is too valuable to waste, since it contains most of the milk sugar (lactose), minerals, and albumen: Scandinavians make a cheese from whey called mysost. We feed it to pigs and chickens; it tends to give goats diarrhea.

As the cheese drips, curds can be stirred occasionally. The more whey removed, the milder the flavour. For a very mild flavour, run cold water over the curds. After drainage is completed, add salt to taste, and it is ready to eat.

A Cheese Press

Here's a design a little bit different from the stan-

dard home-made press, which will allow you to use more pressure as well as pressing more cheese (see pg. 110.)

Basically it consists of an upper and lower one-inch board and four pieces of one-inch dowling rod set into the lower board. The upper board slides up and down on these four legs.

The picture shows a 3-lb. coffee can; for smaller amounts a 2-lb. can is more desirable. Both top and bottom of the can are removed, and for additional drainage a few holes can be punched in the sides. The round follower should be only a hair smaller in diameter than the coffee can, so that it can slide up and down inside the can. I use milk strainer pads so that the curd does not come in

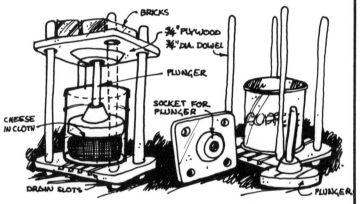

contact with the wood.

Pressure is obtained by putting weights on the top board, which guides the follower down onto the curd and squeezes out the whey. You can use bricks or sand for weight. More pressure (40-60 pounds) will produce cured cheese.

Wash and scald your press after each use to guard the flavour of your cheese.

Cottage Cheese

The first step is to make clabber. This is milk which has been allowed to sour at room temperature. The souring process can take as long as a week during the winter and as short as a day in the summer. Use unpasteurized skim milk or buttermilk only, because pasteurized milk doesn't sour properly. The clabber is ready when it turns to a jelly-like consistency. Cross-hatch the clabber with a knife (fig. 5, p. 109). (Cream cheese can be made at this stage by hanging the clabber overnight in a cheesecloth bag. This separates the curds and whey).

Once cross-hatched, gently heat the clabber in a water bath (fig. 7, p. 111), stirring occasionally. The water should be too hot to touch, but never boiling; the clabber should never get too hot to touch. When the clabber has shrunk uniformly into small pieces, it is done—better underdone than overdone. Personal experience is the best way to get it right. Strain the mixture through a colander. If the curds run through the holes in the colander, it is underdone. If the curds are dry and rubbery, it is overdone. Add a little salt, honey, and cream to taste.

If you can't find rennet tablets in a drugstore or grocery store nearby, they can be ordered from Hansen's Laboratory Inc., 9015 W. Maple Street, Milwaukee, Wisc. 53214 or from Horan-Lally Co. Ltd., 26 Kelfield Street, Rexdale 604, Ontario.

How to Make Hard Cheese
(Makes 1½-2 Pounds)

1. Preparation of the Milk

Allow 4 quarts of evening's milk to ripen overnight in cool place (50-60 deg. F.). Mix in 4 quarts of next morning's milk. This will give a better cheese than if you use all fresh milk; however, milk must taste sweet. You may use either cow's or goat's milk with equally good results.

2. Warm the Milk to 86 Deg. F.

In an enameled or tinned pail, heat milk to 86 deg. F.

3. Add Cheese Rennet

Dissolve ¼ of a cheese rennet tablet in a glass of cold water; to help tablet dissolve, break and crush with a spoon in water; stir until completely dissolved. Put the pail of milk in a larger pail of warm water, 88-90 deg. F.; leave in a warm place, protected from draft. Add the rennet solution; stir milk thoroughly for a minute after rennet is added.

4. Let Set Until "Clean Break"

Let stand undisturbed until a firm curd forms, 30-45 minutes. Test the firmness of curd with your finger; put finger into the curd at an angle and lift. If the curd breaks clean over your finger, it is ready to cut.

5. Cut 2 Ways Vertically—Then 2 Ways at an Angle

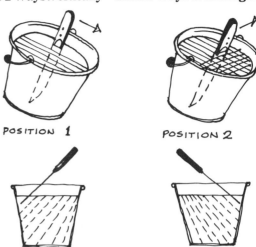

To cut the curd into small cubes, use a long butcher knife or spatula— long enough so that the blade will go clear to the bottom of the pail without the handle dipping into the curd. Cut into squares of about 3/8" as shown in positions 1 and 2 in illustration. Then use your knife at an angle—see position 3 in illustration—starting about 1" from the side of the pail; with angular cuts, slice the curd into pieces about 1/2-1" thick; begin at the top and make each cut about 1/2-1" lower. Then turn the pail and draw similar angular cuts from the other side (position 4).

6. Stir Curd for 15 Minutes by Hand

With your hand, stir curd thoroughly but very gently, with long, slow movements around the pail, and from the bottom up. Carefully cut up the larger pieces that come up from the bottom, but do not squash curd. Try to make the pieces of curd as nearly as possible the same size. Stir continuously by hand for 15 minutes, to keep the curd from sticking together.

7. Warm Slowly for about 1 Hour to 102 Deg. F.

Heat slowly to 102 deg. F. raising the temperature of the curd and whey about 1-½ degrees every 5 minutes. Stir (with a spoon) frequently enough to keep the curd from sticking together. Heating should continue slowly—if necessary a few degrees above 102 deg. F. until the curd holds its shape and readily falls apart when held on your hand for a few seconds without squeezing.

8. Stop Heating. Stir Occasionally for 1 Hour

Remove from heat. Stir every 5—10 minutes, i.e.,

enough to keep curd from matting together. Leave curd in the warm whey until it becomes firm enough so that the pieces in a handful when pressed together will easily shake apart. This will take about an hour.

9. Pour Curd into Cheese Cloth

Pour into cheesecloth 3-4 feet square. Then hold 2 corners of the cloth in each hand and let curd roll back and forth without sticking together for 2-3 minutes to allow whey to run off.

10. Salt Curd

Place cloth with curd in empty pail, sprinkle 1 tablespoon salt over curd, mix well with hands without squeezing; then sprinkle another tablespoon salt on curd and mix well again.

11. Form into Ball and Hang Up

Tie the four corners of the cloth crosswise, forming the curd into a ball. Hang up for 1/2 to 3/4 hour to drip off.

12. Dress the Cheese

Remove cloth from sides of ball. Fold a long cloth, shaped like a dish towel, into a bandage about three inches wide and wrap tightly around ball, forming it into a round shape. Pin in place. With your hands, press cheese down to make the top surface of the cheese smooth. There should be no cracks extending into the center of the cheese. Your round loaf of cheese should not more than 6'' across; otherwise it will dry out too much.

13. Press Cheese

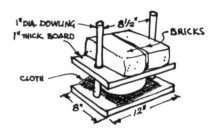

Place 3 or 4 thicknesses of cheesecloth on top and under the cheese. Put the cheese on lower board of press and push upper board down to rest on cheese; place 2 bricks on top. At night, turn cheese over and put 4 bricks on top. Let stand until morning.

14. Paraffin. Store in Cool Place

Remove cloths from cheese and place on board for half a day, turning occasionally until the rind is completely dry. Then dip in paraffin that is heated in a deep pan to 210-220 deg. F. Dip first one half, hold a minute, then dip other half. (If preferred, liquid paraffin may be painted on with a brush, or vegetable or mineral oil may be rubbed onto cheese instead of paraffining.) Then store in a clean, cool but frost-free cellar or similar place. Turn over each day for a few days, then 2-3 times a week. The cheese is usually good to eat after 3-4 weeks.

Some General Hints for Perfecting Your Cheese

If you want a harder cheese:

(1) You may cut the curd into smaller pieces.
(2) You may hold it a little longer, or bring the temperature a little higher when heating the curd (steps 7 and 8).

If you want a softer cheese:

(1) If your cheese becomes too hard, the reason may be that you have used milk which was over-ripened. Be sure it has not stood too long before you make it into cheese.
(2) You may cut the curd into slightly larger pieces.
(3) It may be that you can heat the curd to a lower temperature (step 7), or not keep it heated as long (steps 7 and 8).
(4) Maybe you have used too much weight in pressing.

A Homemade Forge

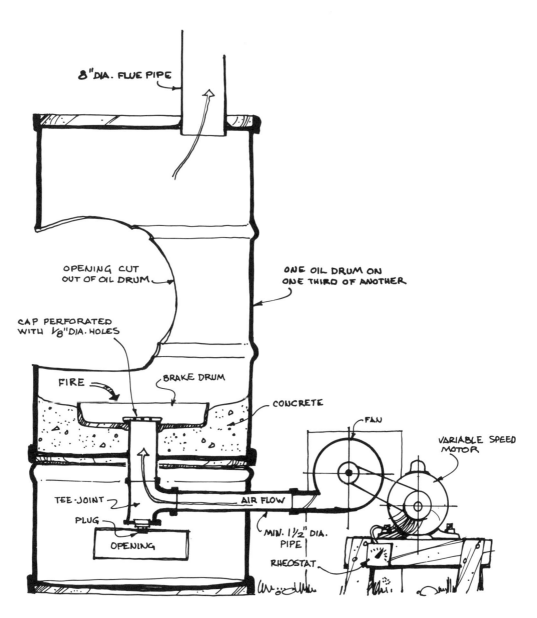

8" DIA. FLUE PIPE

OPENING CUT OUT OF OIL DRUM

ONE OIL DRUM ON ONE THIRD OF ANOTHER

CAP PERFORATED WITH 1/8" DIA. HOLES

FIRE

BRAKE DRUM

CONCRETE

FAN

VARIABLE SPEED MOTOR

TEE-JOINT

AIR FLOW

MIN. 1 1/2" DIA. PIPE

PLUG

OPENING

RHEOSTAT

• SECTION VIEW THROUGH SIDE OF FORGE •

Rural Water Works

by M.J. Reese

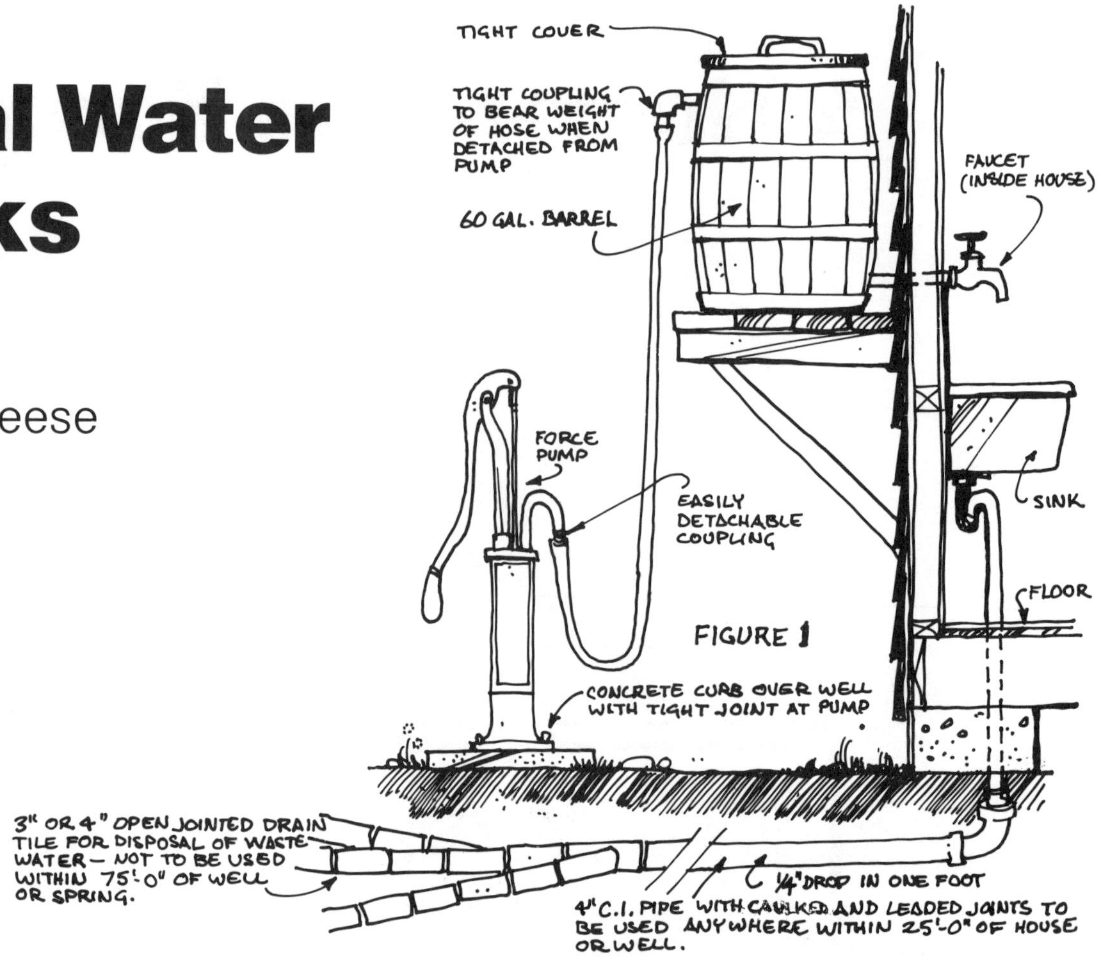

FIGURE 1

TIGHT COVER

TIGHT COUPLING TO BEAR WEIGHT OF HOSE WHEN DETACHED FROM PUMP

60 GAL. BARREL

FAUCET (INSIDE HOUSE)

FORCE PUMP

EASILY DETACHABLE COUPLING

SINK

FLOOR

CONCRETE CURB OVER WELL WITH TIGHT JOINT AT PUMP

3" OR 4" OPEN JOINTED DRAIN TILE FOR DISPOSAL OF WASTE WATER — NOT TO BE USED WITHIN 75'-0" OF WELL OR SPRING.

4" C.I. PIPE WITH CAULKED AND LEADED JOINTS TO BE USED ANYWHERE WITHIN 25'-0" OF HOUSE OR WELL.

¼" DROP IN ONE FOOT

If a well or cistern is located close to the house, one of the simplest and cheapest methods of obtaining running water in the kitchen in the warmer climates is to place a covered barrel or other supply tank on a shelf outside the kitchen wall and in such a position that it can be filled from the pump through a hose, as desired. A pipe attached to the bottom of the barrel or tank and passing through the wall has attached to it a faucet over a sink in the kitchen. The hose is detachable and can be removed from the pump when not in use (fig 1).

The sink is connected by lead pipe through a trap to a drain, which should consist of cast iron soil pipe when it is used anywhere in the immediate neighborhood of the well or cistern. Do not under any consideration use cemented tile for this purpose within 30 feet of any source of water supply. When far enough away from the house or well, this drain can empty into open jointed drain tile which may be placed in the garden soil or any other pervious soil, thus disposing of the waste water by absorption. The disposal tile should have a fall not to exceed 1 inch in 50 feet, else the water will rush to the lower end and water-log the soil. In very porous or sand soils 1 foot of 3 or 4-inch tile per gallon of discharge per day is sufficient. In heavier loam or clay soils, 2 feet of tile are necessary and sometimes more for every gallon. Aeration of heavy soil can be brought about by the use of coarse cinders or gravel laid in the bottom of the tile ditch.

Where there is danger of freezing or where the well is very close to the house, about the simplest and cheapest method is to place a pitcher pump or force pump over a sink in the kitchen. The suction pipe of the pump may be attached to the well or cistern and water obtained when desired merely by pumping. This is provided the vertical distance from the pump to the water in the well does not exceed 20 feet, as under ordinary circumstances a pump will lift water satisfactorily by suction only to about that height. The allowable distance from the well to the pump for this arrangement will vary with local conditions; cases have been noted in which the distance was as far as 200 feet. As water meets with resistance in pipes, due to friction, elbows, and bends, it is well to take off about 2 feet from the allowable vertical pumping lift for every 100 feet the water is drawn horizontally.

The Shower Bath

A cheap and convenient shower bath can be easily made and used in the kitchen or on the back porch (fig 2).

A hole is cut in the bottom of a 4-gallon bucket and a piece of pipe 2 inches long soldered in the opening. Rubber tubing 4 to 6 feet long is attached to the pipe and a nozzle is fitted on the end of the rubber tubing. A sprinkler from a watering can may be used instead of the nozzle. The bucket can be raised or lowered to suit the convenience of the person taking the bath by a rope fastened to the handle of the bucket and run through a pulley which is fastened with a staple to a joist in the ceiling. The end of the rope is looped over a hook, which is driven securely into the window or door facing, or into the studding in the wall.

A clothespin closed over the rubber tubing serves as a stopcock to cut off the water as desired. The shower can be better regulated by using a device such as is shown in the illustration. The end of a piece of No. 12 or 14 wire is fastened to a disk of leather or tin, or a cap of a tin can, by making a hole in the material used, running the wire through and looping the end. This disk is placed over the hole in the bottom of the bucket and the attached wire extends through the rubber tubing and the nozzle. The shower can be regulated by the disk being raised and lowered by means of the wire. The weight of the water in the bucket will form a sufficient seal when no flow is desired.

A large tub is placed under the shower, in which the bather stands.

A Progressive Water System

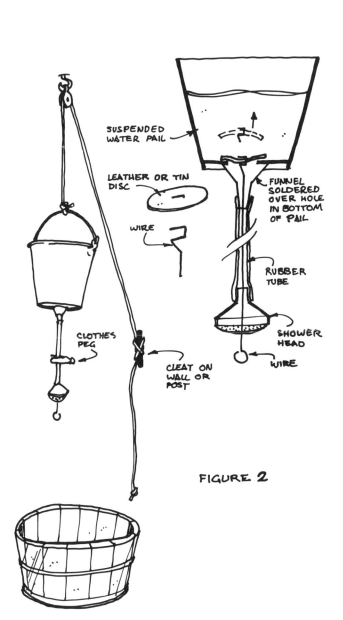

FIGURE 2

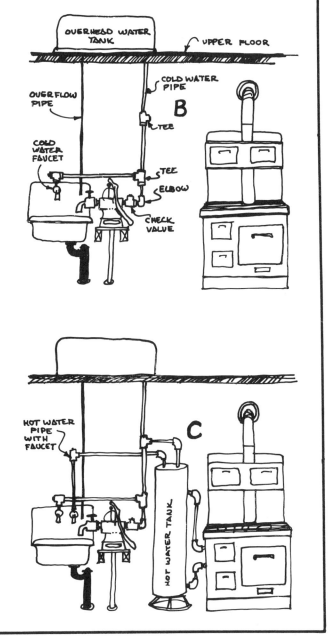

A Hand Operated Washing Machine

by C.C. Pettit and H. Holtzclaw

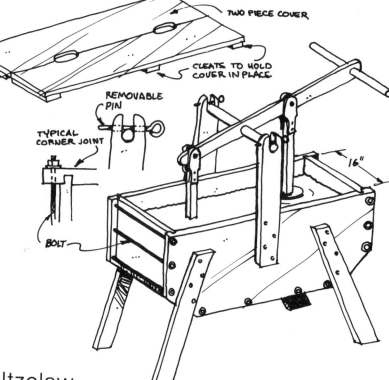

· FIGURE 1 ·

This washing machine reverses the principle used by the usual commercial washer, in which the clothes are swished through the water from various degrees of a circle until the water is moving, and then reversed. In this machine, the clothes stay more or less stationary while water is forced back and forth through the clothes by the piston action of the plungers.

One plunger creates pressure as it moves downward. The slopes at the ends of the tub bottom help the churning action of the water caused by the plungers.

A rectangular tub is best for this type of washing and churning process. In general, a moderately strong wood that will not warp excessively can be used for the tub. The sides should be grooved for the ends and bottom of the tub, as indicated in figure 1, and bolted with threaded rods extending through both sides with washers to draw them tight. The bolting will prevent leaks.

Materials

Tub Construction—moderately firm softwood, free from large heartwood growth.

sides—2 pieces—1" x 18" x 38"
ends—2 pieces—1" x 12" x 16"
bottom—1 piece—1" x 16" x 26"
bottom—2 pieces—1" x 6" x 16"
legs—4 pieces—1" x 4" x 30"
round plungers
    —2 pieces—1" x 10" diameter
    —2 pieces—1.5" x 5" diameter

cover (may be omitted)
    —2 pieces—1" x 8" x 36"
    —6 pieces—1" x 3" x 8"

Operating Parts—moderately firm hardwood

lever
    —1 piece—1" x 3" x 48"
plunger stems
    —2 pieces—1-1/8" square x 15" long
uprights
    —2 pieces—1-1/8" x 3" x 24" long
pivot and handle
    —2 pieces—1-1/4" diameter x 18" long

Metal Parts

plunger connections—
    —1/4" x 1-1/2" x 6" long
    10 rods—1/4" or 5/16" diameter,
    18" long with threads and nuts on each end
    (iron and brass)
    20 washers about 1" diameter with hole to fit rods
    1 rod—1/4" x 6" with loop end for retaining pivot
    6 bolts—1/4" x 2" long
    24 screws—1-3/4" x No. 10, flat head
    50 nails—2-1/2"
    strip sheet metal with turned edge
—2-1/2" wide, 72" long

Small quantity of loose cotton or soft vegetable fibre for caulking seams. Oakum also works well.

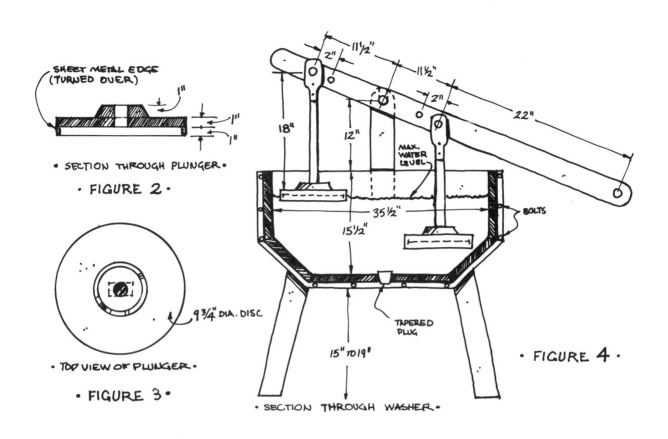

SHEET METAL EDGE
(TURNED OVER)

1"
1"
1"

• SECTION THROUGH PLUNGER •

• FIGURE 2 •

9¾" DIA. DISC

• TOP VIEW OF PLUNGER •

• FIGURE 3 •

11½"
2"
11½"
2"
22"
18"
12"
MAX. WATER LEVEL
35½"
15½"
BOLTS
TAPERED PLUG
15" TO 19"

• FIGURE 4 •

• SECTION THROUGH WASHER •

Construction

(1) Mark and groove sides for end and bottom members.
(2) Drill holes for cross bolts.
(3) Cut off corner and trim ends of side members to
    length.
(4) Bevel ends and bottom pieces to fit into groove in
    side members.
(5) Mitre bottom and end members together.
(6) Assemble and bolt
(7) Cut and install legs.
(8) Caulk seams between ends and bottom members with
    loose cotton or other vegetable fibre (or oakum) to
    make seams water-tight. If joints to side members
    are carefully made, they may not need caulking.
(9) Bore hole and make plug for draining tub in the
    bottom.
(10) Make and install upright pivot members.
(11) Make and install plunger lever. *Note:* The cross pivot
member (round) should be shouldered or notched at each
pivot to prevent side movement.
(12) Make plungers and install (see illustration).

The size described in the drawings is large enough for
an average family in North America. The same principle
may be used for a larger or smaller machine, provided the
basic proportions are maintained. The tub width should
be slightly less than half the length to get a proper surge
of water. The pistons should be wide enough to move

within a couple of inches of each side of the tub. Likewise, the length of the rods on the plungers must be such
that the plungers go well into the water and the clothes
come completely out of the water at the highest position.

Operation

Fill the washer with 15 gallons of warm or hot water, depending on what is available. Remove stains. Rub soap
into the areas of garments like cuffs and collars which
come in close contact with the body. Soak very dirty
clothes before putting them in the washer. Soap can be
dissolved by shaving strips and then heating it in a small
quantity of water before adding it to the wash water. A
six pound load of clothes is the right size load for best
cleaning. Wash at a moderate speed, about 50 strokes a
minute, for 10 minutes or longer, if it seems necessary.
After washing and rinsing the clothes, rinse the washer
clean and replace the stopper. To keep the wood from
drying out and causing the tub to leak, put about an
inch of water in the washer when it's not in use.

Alternatives

The simplest method to wash clothes is to use a
bucket with some sort of plunger device as an agitator. A
drain plunger or a metal funnel attached to an old
broomstick works well and is cheap.

Creative Recycling

by Jeanine Mitchell

Living in a cabin, or even just out in the country, you just naturally get into recycling—for two reasons, actually. First you can't afford a lot of waste, because that means bringing in extra supplies. When you have to carry stuff through the bush on your back, you quickly learn to improvise much of what you need from tin cans, jars, and so on.

Second, you are no longer compartmentalized. In the city, you can do the most atrocious things to the earth—pour Draino, phosphate detergents, paint, pesticides and so on down your drains—and never get your nose rubbed in it. Not for a while, anyway. You never see anything in its wholeness—all is hidden away—no blood on your money, no feathers in your crankcase.

But when you live off the land right under your feet, learn its secrets, listen to its songs, how can you destroy it? Now you have control back, and with it, sanity and responsibility.

There are so many real uses for most waste items, hardly any need be even collected for reprocessing. In the course of making your own, you drastically cut your consumption, which means the planet's wealth can be spread around to other people with nothing. This is only suitable for a whole-world economy, which is overdue anyway.

Newspapers are an exception. Too little is said on too much paper. Look at a city daily—most of it is covered in trash: ads for senseless products, stories that don't tell you anything, pompous editorials. The actual information could be condensed to fill a fraction of the space now used. Radios and televisions should be taking over a lot of the communication work, although not all of it.

You can burn newspaper, rolling it into tight "logs" so it will last a long time: a great fuel for poor people. You can make kites out of it, papier-mache, insulate your house with it, use it for a mulch to keep weeds out of the garden, pack things in it, sit on it, mop up with it.

But at the present rate of consumption, it must be reprocessed in large quantities as well.

You all must know that all your writing paper can be free—just stop throwing away envelopes, paper used on only one side, light-coloured bags, etc. Make note pads by cutting one side paper into pieces and stapling.

Tin cans are a trip. Many uses for the garden alone, including the following: cover young plants at night to protect from slugs and bugs, nail to posts or place around garden to attract magnetic forces of earth, which improves the harvest. Crush cans and bury them in a trench around garden if gophers are causing problems. Hang can lids on branches of fruit trees to help keep away birds. (Note: plant chokecherries, or some other sour or bitter fruit bush nearby, and the birds will eat those instead.) Start plants in them, laying stones on the bottom for drainage. Cut large tins up for bird feeders and bird baths, folding over any sharp edges. Birds eat hungry bugs off your plants.

Store food in cans, to keep it dry, bug- and mouse-free. Make windproof candle bug for night travel, if you live in the bush: cut off one lid of a medium size tin, cut a hole on the middle of one side, attach a wire handle to both ends of opposite side, stuff a candle up through the hole (fig. 1).

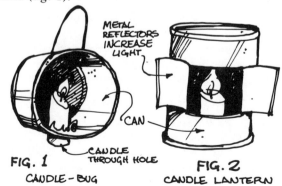

METAL REFLECTORS INCREASE LIGHT

CAN

CANDLE THROUGH HOLE

FIG. 1
CANDLE-BUG

FIG. 2
CANDLE LANTERN

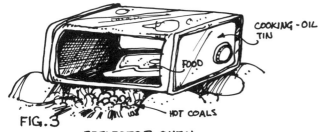

FIG. 3

REFLECTOR OVEN

Or make a candle lantern for bush or house (fig. 2). Makeshift bread pans a la Digger (just cut off top lid).

Pots for camping: add wire handles. **A large square** can (used often for large quantities of cooking oil and found in Chinatown alleys) can become a makeshift reflector oven if two sides are cut out, leaving ends intact. Put food in and place it facing the fire (fig. 3). Cans for camping dishes, too. Bury them when moving on. Cut tins, especially large ones, flatten metal, and save for fishing and building things. Cookie sheets.

Musical instruments: drums, with inner tube or an old skin over one end, wind chimes of tin lids strung together, makeshift steel guitar of wooden frame covered with tin cut from gas can—see *Living on the Earth* by Alicia Bay Laurel.

FIG. 4

Toys: stilts from large cans with string handles (fig. 4). Walky-talky of string tied between two cans; sound travels through string, you talk into the can and hold open end to your ear. Give kids small seafood cans to paint into ashtrays, snack dishes, thingamajigs.

Bottles

Rolling pins, candle holders, vases. Give them to kids to make water xylophones or water flutes: line up ten bottles, with varying water levels, tap them with a stick or blow across the top, and you play songs. Save them to fill again with homemade wine, beer, root beer, juices from your juicer capped for the winter. Make glasses by cutting off the tops and filing the edge, and make bowls and individual greenhouses for struggling plants by cutting tops off gallon jugs. Here are three more-or-less methods of cutting bottles:

(1) Wrap gasoline- or kerosene-soaked length of yarn around cutting point of cold bottle three times. Light, turning bottle slowly, as flame follows yarn. When flame has encircled bottle, turn until it cracks. If it

doesn't break after a moment, tap a little above cutting line with knife handle, repeating the burning if this too fails.

(2) Fill bottle just below cutting line with warm water. Melt paraffin (in a tin can) and let stand till warm. Pour about one-half cup warm wax into the bottle, using a funnel to keep all wax off sides of bottle. Refrigerate bottle until ice cold. Heat rest of paraffin over double boiler until as hot as you can (but NEVER heat wax directly over burner or flame—it can explode), and pour through funnel onto the hardened wax in the bottle. This should crack it to smooth edge.

(3) Buy a cheap glass cutter from hardware store, attaching it firmly to table top or inside a box. Using much force, push and roll bottle away from you against cutting edge of the tool. After circling the bottle smoothly suspend a string with nail or bolt tied to it into the bottle and tap at cutting line gently (or dip in hot, then icy water). File edge, sand edge until frosty looking.

If you plan to cut a lot of bottles, you might want a proper cutter, as the above methods are haphazard, wasting much glass and patience. Some people make a living with their cutter, turning bottles into candles, glasses, and hookahs.

Send $7.75 to—Fleming Bottle and Jug Cutters, 19432 Military Road, Seattle, Washington 98188. You'll get a reliable, adjustable cutter, postpaid.

Jars

Jars are also very useful. Save any screw-on jars with their lids for canning. Paint black and store film dry; and if you knit and have pets or babies in the house, punch a hole through the jar lid and keep your wool inside the jar, feeding through hole in the lid. Place jars over new plants: keeps away slugs and acts as a greenhouse, frost, and stormguard, keeping them moist and warm. If you travel keep food cold but dry with jars full of ice.

Cut off or smash the bottom of a large-based bottle and blow it like a trumpet—hang it by the door as a dinnerhorn. Cut off bottom and hang wooden bead inside for a bell clapper. Alicia Bay Laurel says: jug for the band—stretch some inner-tube ove the open end and secure with a leather thong. Vary the pitch of the jug by pressing and releasing the rubber.

Water carries. Self-waterers for houseplants: fill jar with water, wick(s) in to reach bottom and wrap other end(s) loosely around plant stem(s) just above the soil. Self-waterers for garden plants: poke small holes in lid and put short bits of heavy string, yarn, pipecleaners, then turn upside down by plants. Clothes sprinkler. Sand-salt sprinkler for icy walks. Containers for different size nails and screw, first aid stuff for trips, sewing kits, baking soda for fire extinguishers. Tape heavy jar around outside (to prevent breakage), fill with water and use for fire extinguishers. Tape heavy jar around outside

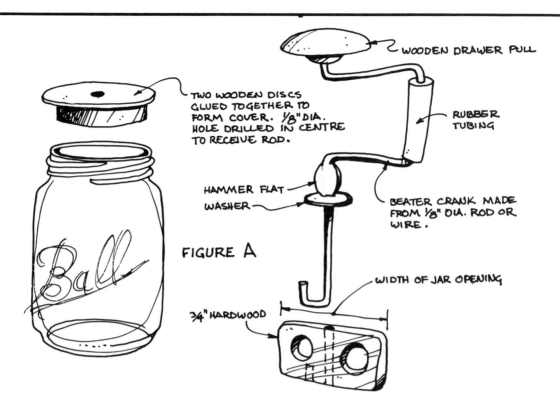

TWO WOODEN DISCS GLUED TOGETHER TO FORM COVER. 1/8" DIA. HOLE DRILLED IN CENTRE TO RECEIVE ROD.

WOODEN DRAWER PULL

RUBBER TUBING

HAMMER FLAT WASHER

BEATER CRANK MADE FROM 1/8" DIA. ROD OR WIRE.

FIGURE A

WIDTH OF JAR OPENING

3/4" HARDWOOD

(to prevent breakage), fill with hot water and use for bedwarmer on cold nights.

Butterchurn: (fig. A) half-gallon jar; for lid, glue smaller disc to larger one—must fit snugly. Drill hole in lid to fit beater rod. Those two holes on the wooden beater are one inch wide. The hole for the rod must fit tight; after passing the rod through it, bend the end up to hold. Rubber tubing is where you turn the beater, just like a drill. Drawer pull is your hand rest. To make butter, fill churn half full of thick cream. Push cover and beater attachment into place, and crank back and forth.

You can also make a food chopper by putting a drawer pull on one end of a dowel rod, fitting an open-wound spring underneath for easier action, poking it through the lid, fitting and wiring two blades (cut from tin cans) on the other end, which rests on a cardboard disc cut to fit the bottom of the jar (figure B).

There are lots of other uses for jars, of course—you can even make a small weather station for farms with jars, scrap wood, assorted odds and ends, and a thermometer.

If you know of more useful ways to cut down on garbage and consume less, send them by carrier pigeon.

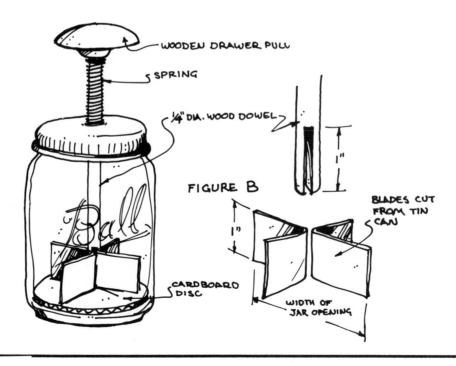

WOODEN DRAWER PULL

SPRING

1/4" DIA. WOOD DOWEL

FIGURE B

BLADES CUT FROM TIN CAN

WIDTH OF JAR OPENING

CARDBOARD DISC

1"

Practical Alchemy & Other Affairs of the Homestead

Eight-year Natural Finish

Raw Linseed Oil	3 gals.
Mineral Spirits or Turp	1 gal.
Burnt Sienna, Oil Colour	1 pt.
Raw Umber, Oil Colour	1 pt.
Paraffin Wax	1 lb.
Penta Concentrate 10:1	½ gal.
Zinc Stearate	2 oz.

Pour the gallon of mineral spirits into a five gallon open-top can. Put paraffin and zinc stearate in another pan and heat over flame, stirring until uniform mixture results. Pour this into the mineral spirits, stirring vigorously. Keep flame away from mineral spirits. When solution has cooled to room temperature, add pentachlorophenol concentrate, then linseed. Stir in colours until mixture is uniform, and it's ready for use. For redwood colour, use ½ pint raw umber, plus one pint pure red oxide colouring oil.

—Mother Earth News

Swedish Farm Paint

Red Iron Oxide	13.0 per cent
Ferrous Sulphate	3.2 per cent
Rye Flour	3.8 per cent
Water	76.0 per cent
Linseed Oil	4.0 per cent

Stir the rye flour into most of the cold water and boil 20 minutes. Dissolve the ferrous sulphate in a small portion of the water and add the solution to the rye flour gruel. Add the oxide, mixing thoroughly. Boil 15 minutes. Just before removing from the fire, add an amount of linseed oil equal to four per cent of the weight of the other ingredients. When cold, it is ready to use.

Quick Drying Paint

A paste is made containing:

Zinc Oxide	100 lb.
Hexamethylene Tetramine	3 lb.
Linseed Stand Oil	100 lb.

To the paste add:
Cobalt drier (cobalt resinate dissolved in an equal weight of mineral spirits) four pounds, and mineral spiris to give brushing consistency.

Filler for Fine Cracks Before Painting

Mix a little flour with the paint to be used to form a soft putty.

Paint for Pine Log Cabins

Formula No. 1
The best finish for peeled pine logs is warm linseed oil. The first coat should be thinned with 20 per cent turpentine; the second coat with 10 per cent turpentine, and the last coat should be straight linseed oil. Allow two weeks to elapse between each coat.

Formula No. 2
Use equal parts of boiled linseed oil and lead mixing oil. Apply two coats.

Paints for Cedar, Cypress, and Redwood

Priming Coat:

White-Lead	100 lb.
Raw Linseed Oil	4 gal.
Turpentine	1¾ gal.
Liquid Drier	1 pt.

This mix makes nine gal. of paint which will prime about 5,400 square feet of surface.

Second Coat:

White Lead	100 lbs.
Raw Linseed Oil	1½ gal.
Turpentine	1¼ gal.
Liquid Drier	1 pt.

Third Coat:

White-Lead	100 lb.
Linseed Oil	3 gal.
Liquid Drier	1 pt.

Barn Paint

Fish Oil, Heavy-bodied, refined	25 gal.
Red Iron Oxide	50 lb.
Mineral Spirits	15 gal.
Talc	5 lb.
Spar Varnish, Neutral	5 gal.

Paint for Buildings

A cheap wash may be made as follows: Take a clean, water-tight barrel and put into it ½ bushel of good lime. Slake it with boiling water; cover it six or seven inches deep, and see that it be thoroughly slackened. Then dissolve the slackened lime in water and add two pounds of sulphate of zinc and one pound common salt. This will harden the wash, and prevent its cracking after application. To colour it: For a cream colour add, in proportion to the above mixture, three pounds yellow ochre; for a lead colour, add a lump of iron black; for fawn colour, add four pounds umber, one pound of Indian red, and one pound lampblack; for stone colour, add two pounds of raw umber and two pounds of lampblack. To render it still more durable, and to give a glossiness to the work, before application to woodwork add a pint of sweet milk to a gallon of the wash.

Paint for Shingles

Slake stone lime by putting into a tub and keeping in the steam. When slaked, pass through a fine sieve, and to each six quarts add one quart of salt and one gallon of water; boil and skim off what rises to the surface. To each five gallons of this result add pulverized alum, one pound; copperas, one half-pound; potash, one half-pound; hardwood ashes, sifted, four pounds; apply with a whitewash brush. This is a very cheap paint and will last for many years.

Whitewash for Masonry

Casein	5 lbs.
Trisodium phosphate	3 lbs
Formaldehyde	3 pts.
Hydrated lime	50 lbs.

Dissolve the casein in 2 gallons of hot water, the trisodium phosphate in 3 gallons of water, the formaldehyde in 3 gallons of water. Add all this to 8 gallons of lime paste, which is made by mixing the hydrated lime with 6 gallons of water.

The lime coating is applied to damp walls, and dries to an opaque, hard, dust-free finish.

Canoe Finishing

Canvas canoes take a good finish, and remain not only water-tight, but also attractive, over a considerable period—if the job is done right.

1. Wash inside and out; then dry thoroughly.
2. Remove old paint, using any standard varnish remover according to the manufacturer's directions.
3. Dry entire canoe thoroughly. For this use a small motor-driven blower, taking warm air from around a heater improvised from one of the common "air-tight" wood-burning stoves. This warm dry air is blown gently into a canvas-covered box completely covering the canoe, the blower being tied in at the end while the other end is left open as a vent. After partially drying the canoe with the stern toward the blower, lift the cover, turn the canoe halfway around, and complete the drying.
4. After making sure that the canoe is dry, and regardless of the final colour desired, prime it with a thin coating—little more than a wash—of aluminum, using a long-oil varnish as the vehicle.
5. Then the canoe is given two colour coats of best grade marine paint, the material for each coat being cut with the addition of ½ pint of turpentine or wood spirits to the gallon as received. After the first coat has dried thoroughly, it is sanded lightly to assure a better bond with the following coat.
6. The job is finished with a coating of spar varnish. The varnish is flowed on with as little brushing as possible, beginning at the keel and working toward the gunwales.

Where any lettering, initials, or decorative design is desired, it is put on over the last coat of colour and covered with the spar varnish along with the rest of the canvas.

Jobs turned out in the manner outlined last from three to five years, depending upon usage (care being taken to drain the craft after each trip) and the amount of abrasion suffered from sandy beaches and rocky shoals.

Mosquito Repellant Oil

Oil of Citronella	16 oz.
Oil of Cedar Leaf	1 oz.
Oil of Pennyroyal	2 dr.
Creolin	4 dr.
Mineral Oil	1 gal.

Mix thoroughly.

Apply a few drops on the hands, face, and other exposed parts of the body and spread lightly over the skin.

More Mosquito Repellant

Oil of Citronella	6 oz.
Turpentine	6 oz.
Kerosene	4 oz.
Phenol Crystals (U.S.P.)	10 gr.

Dissolve the phenol in the kerosene, add the other ingredients, and mix thoroughly.

To keep mosquitoes out of the room, darken the room; saturate blotting paper or cotton with this liquid and place it near the door.

Care of Farm Tools

Carlessness in regard to farm tools, both as regards their replacement after use and their protection from atmospheric exposure during indefinite periods when they are not required, is accountable for depreciation and loss to an extent more than the average farm manager is aware. Necessary tools demand attention just as does any other part of the farm working equipment, and their oversight should be an essential part of thorough supervision. Indeed, they should be included in every periodic machinery overhaul or treatment in preparation for between-seasons storage. A recommended method for keeping both machinery and tools free from rust and in perfect condition for their work after long intervals of disuse, is to give them a coating of beeswax, dissolved in benzol. The benzol speedily evaporates, leaving the steel or iron covered with a thin coating of the protective wax. The advatage of this treatment over the application of paint is that plough mouldboards, shovels, and hoes remain polished and ready for instant work, whercas paint and grease coverings have the effect of making soil adhere. The beeswax coating is equally effective in hot or cold weather, but as benzol is highly volatile and flammable, the mixture should be kept in a tightly-corked bottle and kept far away from any exposed light. Where small tools, such as spanners, bits, and pliers are to be given this treatment, an effective method is to dip them in boiled linseed oil and let it dry on them; or the tools may be warmed on a stove and then smeared with white beeswax, after which they should be heated again to permit the wax spreading thinly and evenly over the surface to penetrate all interstices in the metal. One treatment of the metal of machinery or tools by one or other of the methods described will keep the machinery and tools rust free and bright for as long as a year, if need be.

Hints on Buying Second-hand Tools

Having in my youth worked at the bench for 12 months with an old tool-buyer, and learnt the art with him, I mostly buy all my tools second-hand, and save about 60 per cent, thereby, and tools run into money. The following hints from my experience may help others:

(1) In buying second-hand tools, go round the pawnshops and second-hand places devoted to such.

(2) Know what tools you want, their proper brands, and their present price, new.

(3) Look around each shop as you go in; if the articles you want are not readily procurable, do not waste time stopping.

(4) If they are not, and you see a tool you want, good and cheap, snap it up at once; it will be gone when you want it.

(5) Look carefully at each tool for flaws, and reject any that have been patched up, unless you can patch them up better with little trouble.

(6) Never, under any circumstances, believe anything the salesman tells you as to the tool's quality: the more emphatic the seller, the bigger liar, as a rule.

(7) Do not leave deposits on any tool; buy it right out, or you will most likely have trouble about it later on.

(8) Some salesmen try to bluff a buyer into taking a thing; the minute one starts this game, throw down the tool and prepare to leave; this will bring him to reason.

(9) Carry an up-to-date price list in your pocket; it saves argument.

(10) A fair price for good second-hand tools is 35 to 50 per cent of their new price, according to quality.

(11) All nuts rusted tight, rusty tools, etc., can be fixed up with a little kerosene.

(12) If possible, go round once with a good buyer, and get him to show you how to pick good tools.

Waterproofing Boots

One pint linseed oil, ¼pt. oil of turpentine, ¼ pound beeswax, ¼ pound pitch. Melt ingredients by standing tin container in boiling water away from a fire, renewing hot water till all are blended. The vapour is flammable. When dissolved pour the liquid into a tin to set. When required for use, melt a small quantity and rub well into the soles of the shoes.

Or: Melt in a tin over a low flame 1pt. boiled linseed oil, ½ pound mutton suet, six ounces clean beeswax, and four ounces resin. See that boots are dry and clean, and give a plentiful dressing; it must be put on warm with a soft brush. The leather will become quite pliant and resist all moisture.

Or: Rub a lump of wax on the boots until they become a grey colour, then heat a piece of old linen or soft calico in the oven and smooth over with the hot rag till the leather has absorbed the wax. Allow the shoes to cool, then give a good brushing and apply a good boot polish.

Identifying Poisonous Bottles

A sure way to avoid mistaking a poison bottle for another is to push two ordinary pins crossway through the top part of the cork at right angles, with the points projecting. That identifies the bottle even in the dark.

To Pull Out Stumps

When pulling out a stump with a chain and team only, hook the chain round the bottom of the stump, not the top, with the hook on the opposite side to the team, and pass the chain over the top of the stump. This gives a leverage and increases the pulling power. A better way, with a little grubbing, is to get the chain round a big root, and pass over the top of the stump as before.

To Square a Corner

To square a corner when plotting out the site for a paddock or building, lay a four-foot straightedge along one line from the corner peg, and another of three feet along the adjacent side. Then bring their ends exactly five feet apart and you will have a perfect right angle. From the height and base of the angle, the sides may be then lined out.

To Mend Troughs

To mend tanks or troughs that have pinholes rusted through, fill a kerosene tin with cold water. Throw in washing soda until the saturation point is exceded and undissolved soda can be seen lying on the bottom of the tin. Next get a flat vessel, such as an old baking dish, and mix cement with this water until it becomes a thick paste (make only a small quantity of cement at a time, as it sets very quickly). Apply this paste thickly to the holes with a brush, spreading some around them also. Moisten and wring out a piece of unbleached calico and press it down on the cement firmly and smoothly, as if sticking paper on a wall. Put another coat of cement paste on this, then apply another strip of calico, and a final coat of cement will finish the job. Two people are needed to make it a success—one to mix the plaster, and one to do the work. The person mixing the cement must keep briskly stirring and mixing the paste, turning it over with a small trowel till all is used. Water should be shut off from the tank for twelve hours. The patch will have set hard and will not crack when the tank expands or peel off when dry. Sheep troughs stand

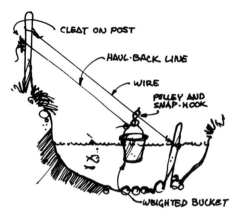

CLEAT ON POST
HAUL-BACK LINE
WIRE
PULLEY AND SNAP-HOOK
WEIGHTED BUCKET

for years after this treatment, and a tank made of flat galvanized iron was successfully treated while full of water. No soda was available on one selection, and waterglass was used to mix the cement, and used while the tank was full of water.

Water Elevator

A length of No. 8 fencing wire is stretched from a post at the top of the bank to a stake driven into the creek bed in such a position that the lower end of the wire will be completely under water. A bucket is suspended from the wire by means of a pulley and snap hoop. A weight must be attached to the side of the bucket in order to sink it. The buket is operated by a rope, either with the hand or with a small windlass.

Fireplace Brick Cleaner

Make a past of:
2 oz. powdered pumice
2 oz. soda
2 oz. salt
plus as much water as is needed to bring it to a creamy consistency. If the bricks are very sooty, add 1 tbsp. of ammonia. Apply with a stiff brush, covering the bricks completely, and scour with a will. Rinse with clear, warm water. Be sure bricks are dry before fireplace is used again.

For a soapstone, sandstone, or chuckanut stone hearth, clean with pure water, then sprinkle on some powdered marble or soapstone, and rub with a piece of stone as large as a brick with one flat side.

Stove Black for Stove Grates

Melt 1 lb. asphaltum in an old tin or kettle. When melted, add one-half pint linseed oil, and one-quarter pint oil of turpentine. Beforehand, clean the grate well. Apply blackening while still hot with a small painter's brush that will get into all the crevices. Leave the grate to dry.

Stove Polish

Add to 1 pt. benzine, 1 oz. pulverized resin. When dissolved, mix any good and finely ground black lead. Use the liquid as you would water for mixing polish. Apply with a small paint brush, rub smooth, as it dries rapidly. When dry, polish with a soft stove brush.

Home-made Fire Kindlers

Melt 3 lbs. resin, 1 qt. tar and stir in as much sawdust and pulverized charcoal as possible. Spread on a board to cool. Break into walnut sized lumps. You can light these with one match—it burns for some time with a good blaze.

Leaky Laundry Tubs

If you have a cement laundry tub, it is probably an oldie—and the older they are are, the more porous and fragile they become. If it begins to leak water through decomposing cement, there's nothing you can do but buy (or make) a new one, since paint won't adhere to the soap-saturated surface. But cracks can be patched really easily. Regular cement mixed in finish proportions (1 part cement to 3 parts sand, or a bit leaner on the sand) is just fine. Undercut the crack to insure good binding—and your oldie will remain a goodie as long as you care.

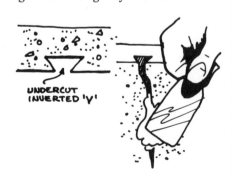

UNDERCUT INVERTED 'V'

Chick Food
(starter and developer)

	lb.
Hulled Oats	10
Corn Meal	50
Wheat Middlings	20
Millet	2
Rape	1-1/4
Caraway	1/8
Gentian	1/8
Ginger	1/4
Black Pepper	1/4
Bone Meal	2
Shell Meal	2
Epsom Salts	2
Dried Buttermilk Powder	10

Have all ingredients finely ground before mixing. Mix thoroughly.

Feed as any standard chick food, giving no more than will be cleaned up at each feeding.

Liquid Manure—Chinese and Japanese Style

Into a sealed jar put a collection of putrid animal substances, consisting of fish, blood, etc., to which is added a certain quantity of urine, but the vessel is not completely filled. It must remain sealed in this vessel for six months. Before using, it is always diluted with four or five times its bulk of water and it is used extensively for garden crops, but universally in drills.

Non-slip Log Sawhorse

Refitting Axe Handles

A new axe handle, as purchased in the store, often does not fit an axe head. It was made for use in a number of heads, and thus needs to be shaped. A wood rasp is probably the best tool to do the job.

The handle should fit the axe eye snugly at all points Never drive a nail in the end of the handle after it has been fitted to the head to hold the head on the handle. It will split the wood, and allow the head to slip off. Use a wooden wedge as shown. The wedge should be dry, soft wood. Cut off one inch of grip end of handle so it won't split when driven in head.

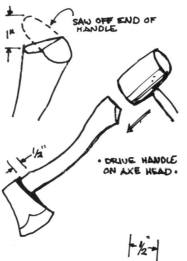

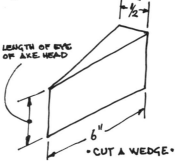

Handle should fit axe eye snugly at all points. Tap in handle to test it for hand.

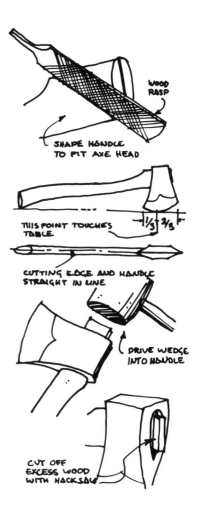

Wedge should be dry, soft wood. Drive it squarely. Soak handle with hot linseed oil.

Sterilizing Soil For Planting

The presence of weed seeds in potting compost interferes with the raising of plants from seeds in trays, pots, and frames. It is therefore advisable to kill off any noxious seeds before sowing. A simple method is to put the earth into a fine-mesh sieve and pour boiling water over it. When the water leaking out at the bottom is uncomfortably hot to the hand the process is complete. Another way is to spread the earth on shallow trays and put it into the oven, turning it over at intervals until it becomes heated right through.

Siphoning Hint

When water has to be drawn from a deep tank by siphoning, and the action cannot be started by mouth suction, hold the end of the long leg of the hose level with the top of the tank, fill it with water and drop it. The suction of the column of water will exhaust the air in the short leg and start the siphon.

Cleaning Bottles

Dirt which cannot be dislodged by hot water or soap and water will probably be loosened by shot or sand introduced with the water. Care must be taken to wash out the shot or sand completely afterwards.

Keeping Bark on Logs

Remove narrow strips of bark from end to end of each piece, one on each side, as soon as the timber is felled (best in early autumn), to allow bark to shrink freely. The cuts and ends should be coated with creosote and the timber seasoned before use.

Bending Wood

In most cases moisture and heat are wanted. Boiling reduces strength, so steaming is better wherever practicable. Bamboos can be softened sufficiently with a gas or spirit flame passed to and fro so as not to burn the surface, which should be wiped over repeatedly with a damp cloth. The object bent should be tied or clamped in the shape which it is required to assume and be left for some days. It will be found useful in some cases to make saw cuts across the grain on the inside of the bend(fig. A), or along the grain (fig. B) at the end of a piece. Any piece selected for bending should have the grain running straight. If it "runs out" at any point on the outside of the bend, there is a danger of the wood slivering-out there.

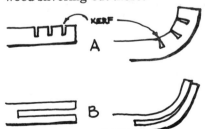

Gate Catch

A is a block of oak or other hard wood shaped as in (a) of the figure below. The latch,*C*, is of the same wood. A long slot cut in *A* allows it to rise on nails sufficiently for *C* to lift it clear when the gate closes. Plate *B*, of metal, prevents a jamming on nail heads.

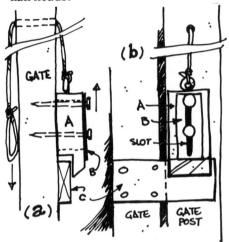

A Self-closing Gate

A gate will swing to of itself if its hinges or hooks be so arranged that opening the gate causes the free end to rise gradually as it moves. If the lower hook be vertically under, but somewhat farther out from the gate than the upper (fig. a), the gate will rise until it is at right angles to its closed position; but if moved through more than a quarter-circle will automatically swing through the next quarter-circle and remain open. This may be convenient in some cases; but usually is not so, and a stop is placed to prevent it opening more than "square." Assuming the two hinges to be of exactly the same shape, the gate is not parallel to the hook side of the hanging post, and the closing post must be inclined somewhat for the gate to touch it top and bottom. This objectionable feature can be overcome if the top hinge has the ring in the centre line of the gate, while that of the bottom is in line with the outer face (fig. b), as the gate can then be hung vertically, though the lower hook is farther out than the upper.

To make a gate swing to through a *half-circle*, the hooks project the same distance from the post, but the lower one is somewhat farther from the closing post than the other (fig. c). If the hinges be similar, the gate will necessarily droop at the closing end. If, however, the lower hinge has its ring farther from the hinge end of the gate than is that of the other (fig. d), the gate may be hung level and yet be self-closing.

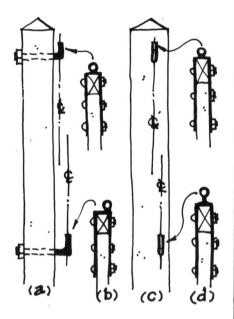

When a Door Sticks

Before cutting, try the effect of a little vaseline or soft soap at the point where the door "binds." Sticking is sometimes caused by a slight expansion due to damp weather, and disappears when the air dries again.

Extinguishing Chimney Fires

Throw some salt and powdered sulphur on the fire, to create fire-killing fumes, and cover the fireplace with a sheet or blanket soaked in water to cut off the air supply and starve the flames. All windows and doors should be closed to assist this. If air can be prevented entering the chimney, the fire cannot last long.

Gate Fastener

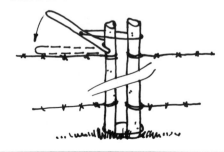

How to Build a Compost Shredder

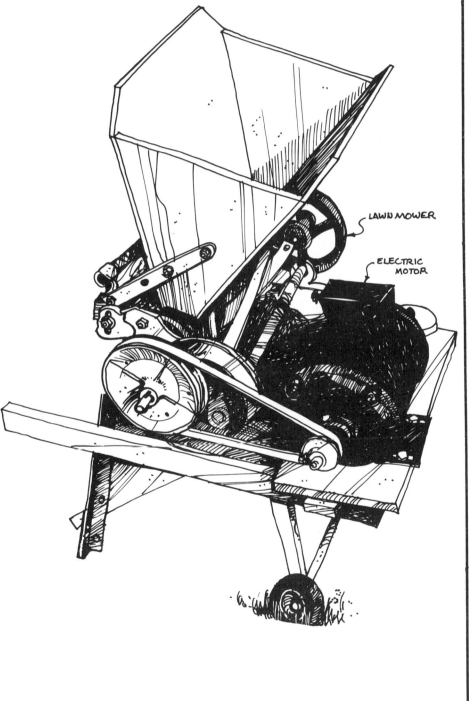

LAWN MOWER

ELECTRIC MOTOR

A simple and easily constructed tool for compost making is the compost shredder. High quality 14-day compost can be made with the shredder. Get an old push-type lawn mower, easily come by from a second hand store for a moderate price.

The Stand

Get some recycled 2x4s so you can build a stand for the mower. The frame has to be built about 20 inches high, perhaps adding a couple of wheels to the front legs for mobility. The size depends on the lawnmower.

The Mower

First remove and recycle the handle and roller from the machine. Then mount the machine upside down on the frame that you've just built. Next remove the wheels (usually by removing the centre bolts, or a couple of cotter pins). This will expose the two small pinion gears, and

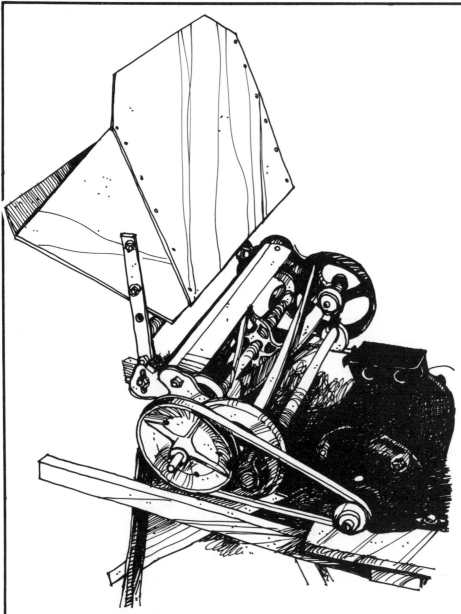

the pair of rectangular "pawls" found in the small slots near the ends of the blade-assembly shaft. Remove all these so that the blades spin freely when given a push in either direction.

The next step—mounting a large 5 inch or 6 inch V-belt pulley on the end of the blade shaft—offers a slight problem. You'll find that the shaft is too short to do so. It will be necessary to have a local machine shop make you a shaft extension fitting that will lengthen the shaft enough for the pulley to be clear of the rest of the machine. The exact dimensions of the piece will depend on the size of the shaft and the diameter of the hole in the pulley. The easiest way to indicate what you need is to take both the mower and the pulley to a machinist and show him what the problem is.

The Motor

To power the shredder, you will need a ¼ or ⅓ horsepower motor (1750 rpm). Be sure to mount the motor in such a position that it will turn the mower blades so that they move TOWARD the cutting bar. If you can't change the direction of rotation of the motor, you can accomplish the same result by putting the large pulley on the other end of the mower-blade shaft. Put a small (1½ inch) pulley on the motor shaft and mount the motor so the two pulleys are exactly in line. V-belts are sold in sizes that indicate their total length. Find the size you need by stretching a rope around both pulleys in place of a belt. If there is no electricity, try an old gas mower as a drive source instead of the electric one.

In order to guide the materials to be chopped to the cutting-bar, make a v-shaped "hopper" of either plywood or sheet metal. It should be about a foot wide at the top and taper to about 1½ inches at the bottom. Make it almost as long as the cutting-bar. Hold it in place by a couple of strips of iron bolted to the roller holders screwed to the ends of the hopper.

The ⅓ horsepower motor shredder can cut up green twigs almost ½ inch in diameter, provided they are fed in slowly. But always remember the damned contraption eats fingers too.

14-day Compost

The keystone of the 14-day method is the grinding or shredding of all material going into the compost pile. Grinding has these effects on compost:

(1) The surface area of material on which micro-organisms can multiply is greatly increased.

(2) Aeration of the mass is improved, because shredded material has less tendency to mat or pack down.

(3) Moisture control is improved.

(4) Turning of the heap is easier.

No layering of material is used in the 14-day method. Material is mixed either before or after shredding, then piled in heaps no more than five feet in height. After only three days, the heap is turned. Turning is continued at two- or three-day decreased intervals. After 12 to 14 days, the heat of the pile has dropped, and the compost is sufficiently decayed for use on the soil.

Jim Buckey, of New Alchemy Institute, West, built the compost chopper and offers the following criticisms and improvements:

1) Mount the chopper on 50 or 30 gallon drum to assure safe flow of compost material—you never know when there might be a rock flying out. Also, as is designed in the article, the compost comes flying out the bottom in all directions, including at your legs and feet. See diagram No. 1.

2) Secure the motor firmly to the stand (i.e. with lock washers) because of vibrations.

3) Use either channel iron, angle iron, or aluminum for making the stand instead of wood. (Get used material.)

4) Extension shafts may be available at hardware stores, so look there first before taking your machine to a local machine shop. (They're expensive.)

5) Use a ¾ horsepower motor, ball bearing, instead of ¼ or ⅓. The smaller ones just don't have enough hp to shred your materials well. Also the ¾ is better built and will last longer.

6) Add a safety bar for the back edge of the hopper to rest on. See photograph on this page.

7) Tack weld a piece of light gage sheet metal to the blades so that the size of the chips can be controlled. Otherwise large pieces of stick will go through the blades. See diagram No. 2.

8) And use a pair of safety glasses, even sun glasses will do. You never know when something might come whirring out.

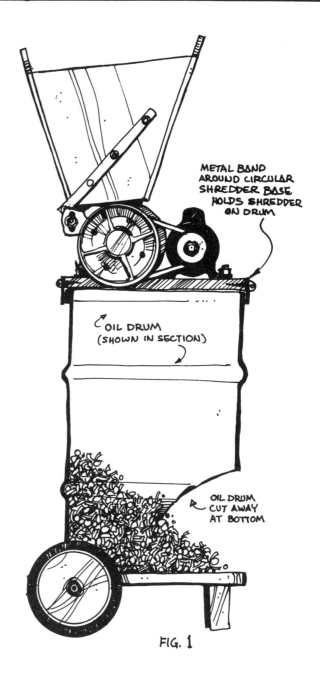

METAL BAND AROUND CIRCULAR SHREDDER BASE HOLDS SHREDDER ON DRUM

OIL DRUM (SHOWN IN SECTION)

OIL DRUM CUT AWAY AT BOTTOM

FIG. 1

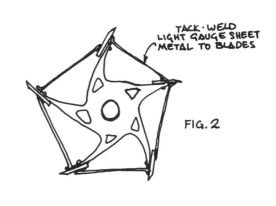

TACK·WELD LIGHT GAUGE SHEET METAL TO BLADES

FIG. 2

Index

CAMROSE LUTHERAN COLLEGE LIBRARY

TH
148
C
628/
25023

CAMROSE LUTHERAN COLLEGE
Library